SMALL WORLD INITIATIVE
Research Protocols
Fourth Edition

Simon Hernandez
Tiffany Tsang
Carol Bascom-Slack
Jo Handelsman

Edited by
Nichole Broderick
Erika Kurt

Small World Initiative Press
crowdsourcing antibiotic discovery

Change the course.

SWI Research Protocols and Guide Bundle ISBN: 978-1-50669-699-7
Component 2 *SWI Research Protocols* ISBN: 978-1-50669-697-3

Authors: Simon Hernandez, Tiffany Tsang, Carol Bascom-Slack, Jo Handelsman
Editors: Nichole Broderick, Erika Kurt
Cover Art: Sarah Jeon, McGill University, 2015.

XanEdu
Change the course.
530 Great Road
Acton, MA 01720
800-562-2147
www.xanedu.com

Contents

Acknowledgments

We thank all the talented and creative people who contributed to Small World Initiative: A Research Guide to Microbial and Chemical Diversity and Small World Initiative: Research Protocols. This version of the guide and protocols is the product of years of writing, testing, and refining by very dedicated people.

We would like to thank Yale's Center for Scientific Teaching for supporting our writers, editors, and partners through this process. The Center helped steer us toward the collaborative efforts that have brought this resource together. We thank the National Institutes of Health's National Biosafety and Biocontainment Training Program for helping to keep our students safe through their review of our biosafety protocols that ensure that we are recommending best practices and our 2015-2016 Science Committee Co-Chairs Samantha Gruenheid from McGill University and Kristen Butela from Seton Hill University for their valuable contributions to these safety efforts. We are grateful to the American Society for Microbiology (ASM) for providing guidance and resources. The spread and streak plate protocols are being used with ASM's permission and were originally published as part of ASM Microbe Library Laboratory Protocols (http://www.asmscience.org/content/education/protocol).

A special thanks to Michelle Legaspi from Yale's Molecular, Biophysics and Biochemistry Department for her critical eye and copy-editing skills and to Gillian Phillips for her chemistry advice. Thanks to all of the Small World Initiative Pilot Partners for their thoughtful feedback and helpful suggestions, but especially Todd Kelson, one of our original pilot partners from Brigham Young University who served as program coordinator 2014-2015, and to other partners whose contributions have transformed this text: Sachie Etherington from the University of Hawaii, Michael Buckholt from Worcester Polytechnic University, Erica Suchman from Colorado State University, Barbara Murdoch from Eastern Connecticut State University, Ann Buchmann from Chadron State College, Ana Barral from National University, Jean Schmidt from University of Pittsburgh, Karen Pelletreau from University of Connecticut, and Neil Enis from Tulsa Community College. We are also grateful to those who have taught with us, in particular, Jessamina Blum and Gabriel Lozano.

We thank Howard Hughes Medical Institute Professors Graham Hatfull, Sally Elgin, and Scott Strobel for inspiring us with their brilliant research courses and their assessment of student impacts and for advising us in development of the Small World Initiative. And finally, we thank all of our students who have participated in this endeavor in its fledgling years and who helped it mature to the worldwide network it has become.

Lab Safety and Best Practices

Knowledge and awareness of the rules for personal and biological safety are essential to create a safe, organized, collaborative, and productive lab environment. Working in the laboratory requires constant surveillance for hazardous materials and practices and training to identify potential hazards and prevent or manage them properly. Lab etiquette informs us about how to behave properly in the lab by developing safe practices and habits and effective responses to potentially hazardous activities and outcomes. Consult your instructor or your institution's safety group for institution-specific instructions.

General Lab Safety and Etiquette

Entering and Leaving the Lab

1. Always wash your hands before and after doing lab work and immediately after removing gloves. Never leave the lab without washing your hands first.
2. Never place personal belongings on benchtops or surfaces used for lab work. Keep clothing, backpacks, and other personal belongings in specified locations.
3. Food and drink are strictly prohibited in the lab!
4. Ask your instructor if the use of electronic devices is permitted. Any electronic devices, including, but not limited to, tablets, iPods, MP3 players, cell phones, and calculators, must be placed in a protective bag (e.g., Ziploc) or other protective wrapping (e.g., plastic wrap). Upon entering the lab, items should be placed in protective bag/wrapping. After the experiment, appropriate procedures for removal and surface decontamination must be strictly followed. Personal belongings that become contaminated with microbiological materials need to be properly sterilized (for example, autoclaved or sprayed with 70% ethanol solution) before leaving the lab.
5. Never remove lab materials, reagents, or cultures from the lab. Lab materials could introduce biologically and ecologically hazardous materials to the environment!
6. Distinguish equipment and supplies on your bench and in your possession at all times. When in doubt about the identity of lab materials, ask your instructor.
7. For your own safety and the safety of others, know where eyewash and emergency shower stations, fire extinguishers, and emergency exits are located.

Personal Protection

1. Wear proper clothing. Closed-toed shoes and long pants are mandatory to enter the lab. Ensure that your hair is held in place or tied back. Avoid clothes that expose too much skin or that are too loose. Clothes and hair can get in the way of flames, lab materials, and experiments.
2. If you are immunocompromised or immunosuppressed (including if you are taking certain medications or are pregnant or may become pregnant), you should consult with your personal healthcare provider **before** beginning this laboratory to discuss the organisms used in this course and the procedures. You should NOT participate in the Small World Initiative unless your

personal healthcare provider has cleared you to do so if these conditions apply to you. If you have skin allergies (e.g., latex allergy), you should discuss with your instructor to obtain nitrile gloves or glove liners. Should you have any minor cuts or broken skin, ensure that they are covered with waterproof bandages. When in doubt, discuss with your personal healthcare provider.

3. When carrying out experiments and handling lab materials, it is mandatory to wear personal protective equipment (PPE):
    a. Gloves
    b. Protective Eyewear (e.g., goggles or spectacles)
    c. Lab Coat

4. Always check gloves for integrity. Gloves provide only a thin layer of protection and may contain holes or pores that could allow the passage of fluids and solid materials.

5. Avoid touching shared surfaces, including light switches, door knobs, handles, and personal belongings, while wearing gloves.

6. When removing PPE, avoid touching the outside of either glove or your lab coat.
   <u>How to remove PPE</u>
   Step #1 – Decontaminate Gloves
   Step #2 – Unbutton Lab Coat
   Step #3 – Remove Gloves (Remember to dispose of used gloves in designated waste containers and not in regular trash.)
   Step #4 – Remove Lab Coat
   Step #5 – Wash Hands
   Step #6 – Remove Eye Protection

Handling Lab Materials and General Precautions

1. Disinfect surfaces before and after each lab activity. Wipe benchtops and large exposed surfaces with disinfectant solution. Disinfectants include 70% ethanol, chlorine bleach solution (commercial bleaches are typically 5.5% sodium hypochlorite) diluted 1:10, or other vetted disinfectants. Never apply disinfectant solution via spray or squirt bottles near an open flame!

2. Handle Bunsen burners, flames, and microincinerators with caution. Before lighting flame, remove flammable objects (e.g., paper, plastic, and solvents) within range.

3. When working with chemicals, such as organic solvents, work in a fume hood as inhalation may cause adverse health effects and never work near a flame or other ignition sources. These materials should be stored in a flammables cabinet or flammable material refrigerator.

4. Avoid bringing samples, cultures, reagents, and hazardous equipment close to the face or skin. Never ingest, inhale, lick, or taste materials in the lab!

5. Practice proper pipetting and never mouth pipette. Never point the pipette toward your body or others. Dispense liquids down the sides of tubes/containers and as close to the content as possible to minimize splashes. Try to avoid dispensing all of the liquid from the pipette as bubbles that pop will cause aerosols.

6. Keep test tubes and microcentrifuge tubes in racks at all times.

7. Minimize aerosols by handling liquid cultures, reagents, and solutions carefully. Avoid excessive shaking and forming bubbles in uncapped tubes when pipetting, pouring, decanting, and mixing.

8. Cap liquids when not in use and always cap when mixing, vortexing, and/or inverting. This measure will help prevent cross-contamination and contact with potentially hazardous biological materials, fluids, and aerosols.

9. Cap/cover samples, cultures, and specimens when not in use and keep in specified locations. Avoid close contact with face, skin, and clothes. Avoid stacking plates and leaving them in the middle of the benchtop when not in use.

10. Label samples and cultures with your name, date, and content (see notes on labeling below). Make sure that all samples, cultures, media, reagents, solutions, used test tubes, microcentrifuge tubes, and conical tubes have proper labeling. Avoid using unlabeled materials.

Disposal

Place used or contaminated lab supplies and chemicals in proper waste containers. Locate the regular trash and specific containers for biological waste, chemical waste, and sharps and broken-glass. Any lab supplies that come into contact with cultures, media, reagents, or any potentially hazardous material should not be left on the benchtop.

1. **Reusable Equipment** – Place used or contaminated reusable equipment (e.g., metal loops, spreaders, glass beads, forceps, and glassware) in proper receptacles for autoclaving prior to future use.

2. **Disposable Materials** – Place used or contaminated disposable materials (e.g., samples, cultures, media, toothpicks, wooden sticks, spreaders, loops, plastic tips, weigh boats, and Petri dishes) in designated biological waste receptacles. This material should be double bagged, sealed when ¾ full, and boxed up for appropriate disposal.

3. **Contaminated Media and Plates** –
   a. Do not remove the lid from plates with fungal growth. Plates with yeasts or molds disseminate spores, which can rapidly spread and contaminate the lab. Consult with your instructor for inspection and proper disposal. Plates should be taped shut and placed in biological waste containers.
   b. Decontaminate broth cultures of organisms using 1:10 diluted chlorine bleach prior to disposal. Depending on your institution's policies, this liquid may be disposed in sink drains after an appropriate contact time or may be treated as chemical waste.
   c. Do not use agar plates (solid media) or liquid media that appear to have bacterial growth/contamination. Consult with your instructor for inspection and proper disposal.

4. **Chemicals** – Dispose of chemicals as chemical waste. Generally, they should be stored in an appropriate leak-proof, sealed container prior to disposal.

5. **Sharps** – Dispose of used sharps (e.g., cutting devices, microscope slides, coverslips, Pasteur pipettes, and broken glass) in designated sharps and broken-glass containers. Sharps containers should be sealed when they reach the fill line (usually around ¾ full) and placed into a biological waste container for disposal.

6. **Large Sharps** – Ask instructor where to dispose of larger sharps, such as serological pipette tips.

Spills & Emergency Response

1. In the case of a spill, immediately inform your instructor.
    a. **Biological Spills** – If there is the potential for an aerosol of the biological materials, alert others and leave the laboratory for 30 minutes to allow the aerosol to settle prior to clean up. Cover the spill with absorbent materials (e.g., paper towels). Add the appropriate disinfectant (e.g., 70% ethanol or 1:10 diluted bleach) from the outside of the spill to the center. Be sure to use the appropriate contact time. Each disinfectant has a unique contact time for each agent. With the disinfectants, volumes, and agents used in this lab, the typical contact time is 10 minutes. Wipe the materials up and dispose of the materials in biological waste containers. Finally, disinfect the cleaned surface one more time.
    b. **Chemical Spills** – For spills of chemicals outside of the chemical fume hood, assess the toxicity and flammability of the chemicals. If toxic, alert others and leave the room. If flammable, turn off ignition sources (e.g., Bunsen burners). Wipe up spill with absorbent materials. You may want to leave absorbent materials soaked with any volatile substances in the fume hood temporarily prior to disposal as chemical waste. Decontaminate the area with soap and water.
2. In the case of skin exposure, the contaminated clothing should be removed and the area washed with soap and water for 15 minutes. In the case of an eye exposure, eyes should be flushed for 15 minutes. Consult your instructor or your institution's safety office for institution-specific instructions and, if necessary, consult the proper medical authorities.

Behavior

1. Always be respectful of your lab mates and their workspace.
2. Do not distract or obstruct lab mates when they are carrying out an experiment. This can compromise their safety and the integrity of their experiments.
3. Communicate questions or doubts about lab safety and proper technique at all times. Also, communicate when others are not adhering to lab safety rules and nonhazardous techniques.
4. Always keep a mental note and written record of your experiments. If you are lost or confused, do not hesitate to ask your instructor for help.
5. Be aware of yourself and your surroundings at all times.

American Society for Microbiology Guidelines for Biosafety

When working with environmental samples, we are always faced with unknown microorganisms. Based on what we know of soil bacteria, most will probably be harmless or nonpathogenic. These bacteria are treated as low-risk (i.e., risk group 1 (RG1) organisms). These are usually contained at biosafety level 1 (BSL-1) conditions. However, bacteria that are normally nonpathogenic may become pathogenic under unusual conditions or environments. Furthermore, we can never disregard the possibility of isolating a pathogen. The isolated soil bacteria that may cause disease in humans are generally risk group 2 (RG2) or risk group 3 (RG3) organisms. These bacteria are usually contained at biosafety level 2 (BSL-2) or 3

(BSL-3) or a combination of these requirements at biosafety level 2 with 3 practices (BSL-2/3), respectively. **We should always treat bacterial isolates in the lab as potential pathogens.**

Another risk of isolating unknowns is increased bacterial load. Every time we plate a soil sample, we are allowing individual bacterial cells to reproduce exponentially under optimal conditions. Colonies contain millions of cells, and in some cases, only a small number are necessary for infection. If you have a greater risk of infections (due to a compromised immune system or prolonged sickness), you should consult with your healthcare provider prior to starting the Small World Initiative.

The following guidelines, based on the ASM *Guidelines for Biosafety in Teaching Laboratories* (2012) contain precautionary measures that we must take when working with unknown isolates:

1. Treat all unknown bacterial isolates regardless of sample source (e.g., nature, household items, and human skin) as potential pathogens or microorganisms that may need BSL-2 containment and, in rare cases, BSL-3 containment.
2. BSL-1 labs may plate bacteria from environmental samples. However, these plates must remain covered and sealed or stored in a secure location. Isolates must remain enclosed at all times and only observed through the lid. After observation, plates must be decontaminated by autoclaving and properly discarding.
3. BSL-2 labs may subculture or transfer unknown bacterial isolates from the original medium (described above) to a fresh medium for further testing.

Adherence to the aforementioned guidelines, along with other best-practice suggestions, aseptic technique, and general laboratory safety and etiquette, will help promote a safe and productive lab environment.

For more information:

- **Please read the ASM** *Appendix to the Guidelines for Biosafety in Teaching Laboratories*: http://www.asm.org/images/Education/FINAL_Biosafety_Guidelines_Appendix_Only.pdf.
- **Please visit the following URL for more information on guidelines for biosafety teaching:** http://www.asm.org/index.php/education2/22-education/8308-new-version-available-for-comment-guidelines-for-best-biosafety-practices-in-teaching-laboratories.
- Emmert. Biosafety guidelines for teaching laboratories. 2013. JMBE. 82, 14. Available at http://www.asmscience.org/content/journal/jmbe/10.1128/jmbe.v14i1.531.

Small World Initiative Nonnegotiable Safety Rules

1. Treat all environmental samples as a source of potentially pathogenic microorganisms.
2. Whenever plating from soil, the use of selective media with an antifungal agent (typically 25 µg/mL cycloheximide) is required. The amount of necessary antifungal agent is dependent on the soil and region and may need to be increased beyond typical usage amounts.
3. Never culture environmentally isolated and unidentified microorganisms at 35 °C or higher.

4. Do not culture environmentally isolated and unidentified microorganisms in broth (i.e., liquid culture). Following identification (i.e., 16S rRNA sequencing), low volume liquid cultures (< 5mL) may be used for biochemical tests and making freezer stocks. However, protocols are available that do not require liquid cultures for these purposes and are advised.

5. Properly dispose of plates with fast-growing microorganisms that spread from a single colony to cover most of the surface of the plate as biological waste.

6. If operating the lab using only BSL-1 practices, cultured plates from environmental samples should be covered at all times and only observed through the lid. For information on how to conduct the lab using BSL-2 protocols, please see our online biosafety resources, in particular "Comparison Chart – BSL-1 vs BSL-2 for Teaching Laboratories" and "How to Transition Your Teaching Lab from BSL-1 to BSL-2."

7. When handling bacteria:
   - Follow "Aseptic Technique" (described below).
   - Wear appropriate PPE and follow the lab safety rules.
   - Keep a reasonable distance between your body and the plate.
   - Keep the lid at an angle over the plate to insert a pipette tip, toothpick, inoculating loop, or any other sterile inoculating supply.
   - Dispose of any used or contaminated supplies in a designated biological waste container or decontamination solution (i.e., 70% ethanol or 1:10 diluted bleach).
   - If your gloves touch any bacterial growth or become compromised, quickly cover the plate, stop what you are doing, dispose of your gloves as biological waste, and thoroughly wash your hands with soap.

8. Do colony PCR and sequencing of unknown antibiotic-producing microorganisms before performing biochemical tests or chemical extractions.

9. Clean the workspace with 70% ethanol or 1:10 diluted bleach solution at the beginning and end of each lab session. Alternatively, another type of disinfectant may be used provided that it is effective against the organisms present and is applied for the appropriate contact time.

10. When in doubt, do not do anything you feel is unsafe and contact your lab safety officer.

Aseptic Technique

Aseptic or sterile technique is a central concept in microbiology and may be the most important part of working in a microbiology lab. The goal of aseptic technique is to promote practices that 1) prevent the contamination of cultures, lab supplies, and equipment with bacteria or fungi from the environment and 2) prevent the contamination of individuals working in the lab with potentially pathogenic bacteria. Aseptic technique requires constant attention until it becomes second nature. Practice and strict adherence to these practices is crucial to making proper aseptic technique a habit. The health of individuals in the lab and the integrity of experiments depend on these principles.

Here are some general guidelines for practicing aseptic technique:

- Remember that bacteria are ubiquitous in the environment and in our bodies.

- Handle lab materials sensibly, avoiding unnecessary motions or contact with contaminated objects/surfaces or things that are not pertinent to the protocol at hand. Package and store inoculating loops, sticks, toothpicks, pipette tips, serological pipettes, agar plates, media, and other previously sterilized materials under aseptic conditions. Should you inadvertently touch any items directly engaged in the protocol, the item is no longer sterile and must be resterilized or discarded (if the item is disposable).
- Keep in mind that Petri dish lids prevent particulate matter and airborne bacteria from contacting the plate surface while allowing the diffusion of air around the edges. Whenever a plate lid is removed, it should be held over the plate as a shield. Do not place the lid face down on the benchtop; avoid placing it on the bench all together. Do not leave plates uncovered. Do not walk around the room with an open plate.
- When working with cultures in test tubes, work diligently and as fast as possible. If Bunsen burners are available, pass the uncapped mouth of glass test tubes through the flame to heat sterilize the opening prior to pouring. This is not necessary, however, and should not be done with plastic test tubes. Keep tubes open for a minimum amount of time. While lids are removed, hold the tube at a slight angle so that airborne contaminants cannot fall into the open tube. Point tubes away from your face and body while working with them.

Labeling

Labeling materials and supplies is a critical aspect of science. With multiple plates, tubes, and samples, it is easy to become confused and lose track of things between and within experiments without the proper labeling practices.

Here are a few guidelines for labeling:

- Always label items that are not going to be used and disposed of immediately.
- Always label the bottom of the Petri dish, never the lid, because the lid may become separated from the actual dish containing the growth medium (e.g., if plates are dropped).
- Always add a date. Dates are informative about when the experiment was performed and provide information about the quality of materials.
- Write as legibly as possible – others may need to find your materials or experiments.
- Label experiments with your initials, experiment number, and number of trials. For example: AF 2.1 – Alexander Fleming experiment 2 performed the first time.
- Label isolates with your initials, type of medium used, and an identifying number. For example: MM-PDA-5 stands for Moldy Mary, potato dextrose agar medium, isolate number 5. If the identity of the organism is known, label with scientific nomenclature (i.e., genus, species, and type).
- For chemicals (e.g., organic solvents, bleach, and ethanol), the following information should be placed on the secondary container: the chemical name, the hazard warnings, the specific physical/health hazards and target organs, the percentage of the chemical in solution, and the date created to maintain compliance with the Globally Harmonized System for Hazard Communication. This information can be found on the Safety Data Sheet (SDS) for the chemical.

Recordkeeping & Data Collection

An important aspect of scientific research is effectively communicating findings to other people. Today's scientific problems are not solved in isolation but rather by groups or communities of researchers working together or building on the results of others. Methods of communication include publication in peer-reviewed journals, presentation of results at public forums through posters or seminars, submission of data to databases, such as GenBank, and communication to the public through media outlets or informal gatherings. To be accepted by other scientists, research results must be reproducible. Good recordkeeping is imperative for ensuring that others can replicate experimental procedures. The Small World Initiative is a real research project with a worldwide community of student researchers. To this end, it is important to keep accurate records. This includes the uploading of required information to the Small World Initiative database (www.smallworldinitiative.org/data), documenting experimental procedures in lab notebooks, and recording digital photographs of results.

Small World Initiative Data Collection Tools:

It is important to collect data to assist in achieving the Small World Initiative's collaborative goals, including tracking samples for additional screening. This information will be shared with student researchers upon request. Data collection tools are provided on the Small World Initiative website: www.smallworldinitiative.org/data.

- **Soil Sample Database** – You should create an account and upload detailed information about your soil samples to this database. In addition to serving as a recorded account of your research, these data will be invaluable for our screening laboratory and for continued research. Don't let your important research results go unnoticed. Record your data in our online database!

- **Laboratory Data Collection Summary Form** – You may use this form to track how many isolates are making it to each stage of your lab work and compare with other researchers. This information helps to flag and troubleshoot any issues and provides valuable data for SWI's screening laboratory. Typically, this information is aggregated by instructors before sharing online. Ask your instructor for more information.

Laboratory Data Collection Summary Sheet

While you conduct your research, you may wish to track the following information to compare with other researchers. **Upload your findings online: www.smallworldinitiative.org/data**

General Metrics: Isolates

# of bacterial isolates picked	
# of isolates tested for antibiotic activity	
# of isolates positive for antibiotic activity	

Spectrum of Activity

# of isolates with activity against each strain/# of isolates tested against each strain:								
Gram-positive				Gram-negative				
Enterococcus raffinosus	Bacillus subtilis	Staphylococcus epidermidis	Mycobacterium smegmatis	Acinetobacter baylyi	Escherichia coli	Erwinia carotovora	Enterobacter aerogenes	Pseudomonas putida
/	/	/	/	/	/	/	/	/

# of isolates with positive activity against "n" tester strains								
1	2	3	4	5	6	7	8	9

Activity Against Gram-Negative & Gram-Positive Bacteria

# of isolates positive for only Gram-positive activity	
# of isolates positive for only Gram-negative activity	
# of isolates positive for both Gram-positive and Gram-negative	

Sequencing

# of isolates sent for 16S rRNA sequencing	
# of isolates with definitive sequencing results	

Extracts

# of isolates on which extraction attempted	
# of extracts produced in sufficient quantity for antibiotic testing	
# of extracts tested for antibiotic activity	
# of extracts confirmed to have antibiotic activity	

Chemical Structure

# of chemical structures determined	
# of novel chemical structures	

Additional Assay Summaries from Your Class (below are two examples):

# of isolates/extracts with hemolytic activity	
# of isolates/extracts with eukaryotic activity (specify anti-fungal, lethal to C. elegans, etc.)	

Tips for keeping a laboratory notebook:

- Notebook entries should be made in ink and in chronological order. Entries should not be erased or covered up. If an entry contains an error, a line should be drawn through the error and new text should continue in the next available space. If using an electronic notebook, entries should be signed electronically when complete.
- Start each entry with a title and a clear description of the objective of the experiment.
- Date each experiment. The dates indicating when the work was begun and completed should be recorded.
- Record all materials used in the experiment.
- Record experimental design and protocols used. Any modifications to existing protocols should be thoroughly explained. Never assume that any protocol is common knowledge. Be sure to write your own descriptions and definitions.
- Record all data collected and observations made in the experiment. If possible, include photos and diagrams.
- At the end of the record, evaluate your experimental results in an interpretation or discussion section. Draw conclusions and future directions if possible.
- Explain all abbreviations and terms that are nonstandard. Explain in context, in a table of abbreviations, or in a glossary.
- Document everything; take detailed notes and photographs during lab. Immediately download and annotate photos to capture accurate data.
- Record negative results. Scientists, especially novice scientists, can learn a great deal from negative results. Reviewing the protocol, brainstorming about where the error occurred or reasons for the negative results are key learning moments. Take advantage of them.
- In general, a good practice is to make PowerPoint slides as soon as you obtain data. Summarize protocols, experimental designs, and results; make presentable tables; and incorporate the photos taken during lab.

Safety & Reminder Symbols

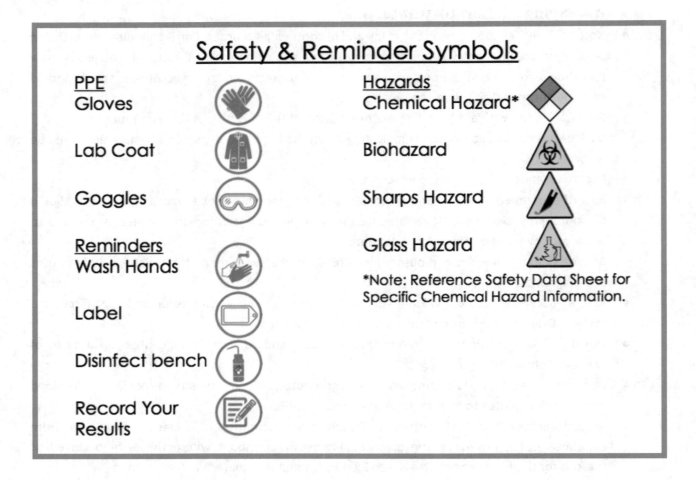

PPE
Gloves

Lab Coat

Goggles

Reminders
Wash Hands

Label

Disinfect bench

Record Your
Results

Hazards
Chemical Hazard*

Biohazard

Sharps Hazard

Glass Hazard

*Note: Reference Safety Data Sheet for
Specific Chemical Hazard Information.

Agarose Gel Electrophoresis

Agarose gel electrophoresis is a common technique in molecular biology and microbiology that allows scientists to separate DNA fragments based on three features: (1) charge (positive versus negative), (2) size in base pairs (bp), and (3) conformation (linear versus circular). Scientists use agarose gel electrophoresis to follow up on DNA extraction and amplification protocols, such as polymerase chain reaction (PCR), which generate millions of DNA fragments. Running a DNA solution or reaction through an agarose gel gives us the ability to separate millions of DNA fragments and analyze them in discrete bands by size, quantity, and quality.

An agarose gel is a jellylike material made up of agarose, a polysaccharide extracted from seaweed, and a buffer solution. Agarose forms a porous matrix that allows molecules to pass through with some impedance determined by the concentration of the agarose and size of the molecules. When the gel is placed in an electric field in buffer solution, charged molecules migrate through the gel toward the opposite charge. One such molecule is DNA, which has a partial negative charge on the phosphate group of the DNA backbone. DNA molecules loaded into the negative end of a gel migrate toward the positive end. Since the gel matrix impedes flow, smaller molecules will travel rapidly, easily slipping through pores in the matrix, whereas larger molecules will be slowed down as they bump into the gel matrix; this process spreads the DNA molecules through the lane based on their size.

Figure 1. An agarose gel with a 1-kb ladder reference. A 1-kb ladder consists of fragments of DNA that differ in size by 1000-bp (1 kb) increments. It is used as a standard for comparison of unknown samples. In this gel, the 1-kb ladder is in the left-most lane, and the other three lanes contain samples with discrete bands that represent DNA molecules that are approximately 1500 base pairs (bp). DNA migrates through the gel in a buffer solution from the negative terminal to the positive terminal when an electric field is applied.

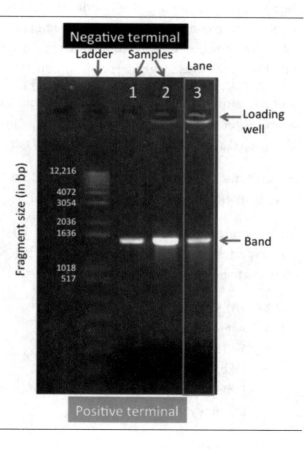

A PCR product, which contains millions of copies of one specific stretch of DNA, will appear as one discrete band on a gel. Nevertheless, a solution containing a mixture of DNA fragments of different sizes will generate either multiple discrete bands or a smear of randomly sized fragments. To estimate the size of the fragment in each band, a molecular-weight size marker or DNA ladder, which contains DNA fragments of known sizes, is run in its own lane on the same gel with the unknown samples. This way, scientists can use gels to analyze mixed samples or PCR products, given that they have a basic understanding of the DNA sample or product at hand. Amplifying regions of bacterial DNA, such as the 16S rRNA gene, through PCR will generate fragments of approximately 1500 base pairs (bp) or smaller. Therefore, we would expect to see one band that has traveled the same distance as a 1500-bp band on the ladder. Any other result, such as a missing band, multiple bands, or a smear, may indicate that the original PCR reaction was not executed properly or that the template DNA did not contain the desired template. Hence, this technique may serve as confirmation that the predicted product was synthesized.

How is it possible to visualize the DNA in the gel in the first place? Scientists use various fluorescent tags that emit light when they bind to DNA. One such tag, ethidium bromide, fluoresces with an orange color when exposed to ultraviolet light. Ethidium bromide molecules intercalate into DNA, or insert between adjacent base pairs, which disrupts the DNA molecule. In living cells, ethidium bromide can produce mutations. (Note: The use of ethidium bromide is minimized because of its ability to produce mutations, which can lead to cancer in animals. The use of precautions, including wearing proper personal protective [PPE] equipment, is necessary to handle this compound.) The brightness given off by the fluorescing ethidium bromide is indicative of the relative quantity of DNA with which it is associated – a bright band contains more DNA than a dim band. While these observations only yield approximations of DNA size and concentration, they serve as a useful first step in determining the outcome of a reaction or confirming the presence of a specific product.

Note: Agarose gel electrophoresis is a variable technique. This particular protocol provides guidelines for agarose gel electrophoresis using ethidium bromide.* Ethidium bromide should be handled only in designated areas and strictly requires use of lab coats, gloves, and goggles.

*Substitutes for ethidium bromide include SYBR safe and GelRed, which is more sensitive and stable than both ethidium bromide and SYBR safe.

Note: Different tags and stains may require different viewing trays and safety precautions. Chamber and gel tray sizes may also vary depending on the equipment available at your facility and the number of samples to be analyzed.

MATERIALS
- Agarose
- 1× TBE (TRIS-borate-EDTA) buffer
- 1-kb ladder
- Ethidium bromide (1% solution in deionized [DI] water)
- Erlenmeyer flask

- Microwave oven
- 6× loading dye
- Gel tray, comb, chamber, and power pack for electrophoresis
- UV chamber or lamp

PROTOCOL

> ### Additional Safety Information
> - Remember to label chemical solutions that will not be used or disposed of immediately.
> - Agarose gels made with ethidium bromide should be disposed of as chemical waste. Generally, they should be dried in an appropriate leak-proof, sealed container prior to disposal. Consult your instructor for institution-specific instructions.
> - **Warning:** Ethidium bromide is a DNA-intercalating agent and therefore is a mutagen. Handle this compound only in designated areas and with care. Wear PPE and avoid skin contact.
> - **Warning:** Do not look directly at the UV light used to illuminate the agarose gel. UV-specific, protective eyewear or special shielding should be used at all times when using UV light as this wavelength of light is damaging to your eyes.

1. Weigh 1 g of agarose and mix with 100 mL 1× TBE buffer in an Erlenmeyer flask. This will make a 1% agarose gel.
2. Microwave contents of Erlenmeyer flask (1-2 min) until the mixture boils or becomes transparent.
3. Allow mixture to cool (10-15 min).
4. Carefully add 2-3 µL of ethidium bromide to cool agarose mixture.
5. Pour mixture into gel tray with appropriate comb and allow 20 minutes to solidify.
6. Carefully pull comb off gel. Place gel tray into gel electrophoresis chamber, submerged in 1× TBE buffer, and start loading wells:
   a. Load 1-kb ladder into first well.
   b. Mix 5 µL of PCR product with 1 µL 6× loading dye and dispense into wells.
7. Plug electrodes on appropriate terminals of the chamber (positive with positive, negative with negative), ensuring that DNA is loaded on the negative end of the gel. What will happen if you plug the electrodes backward?
8. Allow gel to run for 40-60 minutes (at 100 mA/V or constant voltage at approximately 180 V, depending on the equipment).
9. Finally, carefully remove gel from tray and place in UV chamber to get a photograph (expect to see continuous band at about 1.5 kb for full-length 16S rRNA gene).

Aligning and Combining 16S rRNA Gene Sequences

To determine an isolate's species and genus, students can use PCR sequencing of the 16S rRNA gene (see "Colony PCR") and NIH's Basic Local Alignment Search Tool (BLAST, see "Analyzing Sequences with BLAST Search").

To obtain a preliminary identification of isolates, a single forward sequence can be used. First, follow one of the "Colony PCR" protocols, lysing cells and amplifying the 16S rRNA gene. After purification, add the 27F primer and send the mixture to a sequencing facility. Visit www.smallworldinitiative.org to access the "PCR and Sequencing Troubleshooting Guide" for help in addressing common reasons for unsuccessful PCR and suggestions for accurate interpretation of sequencing results. The website also provides detailed instructions on how to send samples for sequencing at Yale University and the University of Connecticut. Note: Be sure to follow your instructor's guidance regarding any rules and regulations for shipping samples. Follow the instruction for "Analyzing Sequences with BLAST Search" to view the alignment of your sequence with the closest sequence matches from the BLAST database.

Your preliminary analysis will usually provide you with between 500-750 bp of coverage of the 16S rRNA gene. The 5' end of the 16S rRNA gene has many more variable regions and provides more reliable identification than the 3' end of the gene. However, you may want to obtain full-length sequencing coverage of the gene to confirm the identity of an isolate. To do so, additional regions of the 16S rRNA gene, both in the forward and reverse direction, should be performed. This requires using the remainder of your initial product from the "Colony PCR" or repeating the procedure for 16S rRNA gene PCR amplification. At the sequencing step, prepare a sample for each primer to be used covering different regions of the gene. Some good options to start with are 27F, 515F, 769R, and 1492R. Sequences for these primers can be found in the "PCR and Sequencing Troubleshooting Guide.")

After sending these samples to a sequencing facility and obtaining the results, trim the sequences as described above. You can then use several online tools to align these sequences into a single contig. First, in order for the forward and reverse sequences to align, enter the reverse sequences into the revseq tool (http://emboss.bioinformatics.nl/cgi-bin/emboss/revseq), selecting "Yes" for both the "Reverse sequence?" and "Complement sequence?" options. The results should be an inversion of the original sequence, and each base from the original sequence should be replaced by its complement (G becomes C, C becomes G, etc.).

Next, align the forward sequences in order to create a forward consensus sequence. For this process, you can use a sequence alignment program provided by your instructor (e.g., Sequencher or BioEdit) or a free online program (e.g., MUSCLE (http://www.ebi.ac.uk/Tools/msa/muscle/) or T-Coffee (http://www.ebi.ac.uk/Tools/msa/tcoffee/)).

If using the MUSCLE page, paste each of your forward sequences preceded by their names in FASTA format (e.g., >AH_LB2_1-27F) and select ClustalW for output format. (T-Coffee has a similar interface but provides multiple output formats for visualization.) The results page will show an alignment of the three sequences. Any position at which all three sequences have the same base will be indicated by an asterisk (*), which will appear on a line below the sequences.

From this report, a consensus sequence can be created. First, paste one of the three forward sequences into Microsoft Word (or another text editor). Next, start at the beginning of the ClustalW alignment and examine each position for which there is no asterisk (not a perfect match of the sequences). If two of the sequences agree and the third does not, select the base that appears in two of the three sequences and make sure that the consensus sequence in your Word document contains this base in this position. Continue this process for each of the positions where an asterisk does not appear. (Note: If you did not trim your sequences prior to analysis, your consensus sequence may have disagreements between the sequences near the beginning and end of the sequence due to predictable sequencing errors. These should be trimmed when creating the consensus sequence).

Repeat this process for the reverse sequences.

You should now have two consensus sequences, one for the forward direction and one for the reverse direction. These can be combined into one final consensus sequence. As described above, use MUSCLE to align the sequences and identify where they differ. You will likely find that the forward and reverse sequences have a large region of nearly perfect consensus in the middle and that the forward has additional bases at the beginning of the sequence while the reverse has additional bases at the end of the sequence. To combine these two sequences, simply copy the extra bases present at the beginning of the forward sequence and paste them at the beginning of the reverse sequence.

Submit this final consensus sequence to BLAST using the above procedure. If the sequence is at least 98.5% identical to a species in the database, then you have identified the genus and possibly the species of your isolate.

Analyzing Organic Extracts for Antibiotic Production

Separations have been a central theme in our research course: we have separated microbes from their natural habitat in our sample collections, we have separated individual cells in spread-and-streak plates, and now, our goal is to separate their bioactive compounds to be studied in isolation. This reductionist approach enables us to study cells, reactions, and metabolites under conditions that reduce confounding variables (other cells or molecules). Separating a bioactive compound from other molecules present in a culture is the first step in determining that compound's physical and chemical properties, mode of action, and activity spectrum. Just the way we use many household products to remove stains on fabrics and surfaces, we can apply specific solvents to cultures to extract compounds with similar properties. These compounds are typically classified based on their **polarity**, a chemical property discussed in greater detail in Section 9. Polar or water-soluble compounds are at one end of the polarity spectrum while nonpolar or fat-soluble compounds lie at the opposite end. Chemists typically like to use solvents that have intermediate polarity to extract a compound of interest without getting all the "junk" at the extremes, such as water-soluble nutrients and long-chain fatty acids. In this protocol, we will use one of two common solvents, ethyl acetate or methanol, to attempt to separate the bioactive compound from most cell components and nutrients in our cultures. Whether the bioactivity is retained in water and/or ethyl acetate indicates the polarity of the active molecule and suggests ways that the compound or compounds can be manipulated in future experiments. ***For more information on chemical extractions, please refer to Section 9 of the *Research Guide*.***

SESSION 1 – PREPARING PLATES

MATERIALS
- One medium plate per isolate (same as isolate's original medium)
- Sterile plastic inoculating loop – 1 per isolate
- Streak plates of isolates (or original master plate)

PROTOCOL

Additional Safety Information

- Remember to use aseptic technique.
- Remember to label chemical solutions that will not be used or disposed of immediately.
- Ethyl acetate and methanol should be:
  - Disposed of as chemical waste,
  - Handled in a chemical fume hood to prevent inhalation, which can cause adverse health effects, and
  - Kept away from flames or ignition sources due to flammability.

1. Select isolates to be cultured for chemical extraction (1 or 2 per student).
2. Obtain streak plate of isolates or original master plate if streak plates are missing.
3. Using the large end of the sterile loop, collect enough single colonies of isolate to spread on the entire surface of a media plate (fill about half of the loop).
4. Gently inoculate entire surface of the fresh media plate by rubbing the loop with colonies back and forth until the entire area is covered.
5. Ensure the plate is evenly coated with inoculum. If needed, turn the plate 90° and continue to rub the loop back and forth. This will grow into a **lawn** of your isolate.
6. <u>Incubate plates at 28°C</u>, or temperatures and conditions specific to isolate. Incubate until next lab session (2 days to a week).

SESSION 2 – CHOPPING UP PLATE

MATERIALS
- Glass bottles (with cap, 100-mL or 250-mL) – 1 per isolate
- Microspatula or cutting device
- Freezing compartment (either a freezer (-20°C or -80°C) or a dry ice/ethanol bath)

PROTOCOL

1. See Additional Safety Information above. Obtain inoculated media plates from previous session. Ensure your isolates have adequately grown into a dense lawn.
2. Using a microspatula, cut the media plate with fully grown isolate into small pieces, about 1 cm^2 each (no need to make precise cuts).
3. Scoop all the pieces with microspatula into the glass bottle and label with isolate name. Push all the pieces to the bottom of bottle with microspatula.
4. Freeze bottle in freezing compartments. Follow specific instructions for freezer compartment of choice below:

   FOR FREEZER, place bottle in freezer until next lab session. (CONTINUE TO **SESSION 3-A** IN THE SUBSEQUENT LAB PERIOD.)

   FOR DRY ICE/ETHANOL BATH, place bottle into bath for 20-30 minutes. (**Caution:** Ethanol with dry ice is supercooled to temperatures that can cause frostbite upon contact with skin. Do not splash ethanol. Place bottles into bath gently to keep glass from shattering!) (CONTINUE TO **SESSION 3-A** IN THE SAME LAB PERIOD.)

Question: What is the purpose of freezing the pieces of agar?

SESSION 3-A – ORGANIC EXTRACTION PART 1

MATERIALS
- <u>Ethyl acetate</u> or methanol
- Deionized water (not recommended for methanol extraction)
- Pasteur pipettes (glass) and bulbs
- 20-mL scintillation vial or other glass container* – 2 per isolate
- Analytical scale (optional)
- Fume hood
- Recommended: drying system or vacuum

Note: As a general precaution, always use glassware instead of plastic when working with solvents.

PROTOCOL

Note: Unless otherwise noted, all steps in this protocol apply to both ethyl acetate and methanol. Ethyl acetate-specific instructions are underlined. Methanol-specific instructions are bold and in red. Pay close attention to differences in the text.

Note: Keep away from Bunsen burner or flame when working with open bottles or beakers with flammable solvents, such as ethyl acetate and methanol.

1. Remove bottles from freezer OR dry ice/ethanol bath. Bottle may be thawed or kept frozen for next step.
2. FOR ETHYL ACETATE EXTRACTION: Add 15 mL of ethyl acetate and 10 mL of water to bottle. You may notice two layers will start to form. The top layer is the organic (ethyl acetate) phase, and the bottom layer is the aqueous phase.
   What does the placement of layer say about the density of ethyl acetate?
   Place capped bottle on shaker at room temperature until next lab session.

   OR

   FOR METHANOL EXTRACTION: Add 15 mL of methanol to bottle – DO NOT ADD WATER! – and place capped bottle on shaker at room temperature until next lab session.

   Note: Methanol and water are intermiscible, which means they can mix together. Mixing methanol with water will dilute your extract and will make it difficult and time consuming to dry the extract.

While shaking at room temperature, bottle will thaw and organic solvent will extract soluble components in the lawn and agar.

SESSION 3-B – ORGANIC EXTRACTION PART 2

1. Using a Pasteur pipette and bulb, gently transfer all the liquid from the bottle to a labeled scintillation vial or other glass container. Once all liquid is transferred, let sit for 2-3 minutes to allow any debris to settle (e.g., small chunks of agar).

<u>FOR ETHYL ACETATE, organic (top) and aqueous (bottom) layers will start to separate. Depending on the color of your extract, both layers may appear clear. Carefully identify the interface between them.</u> **Note:** <u>Emulsion (a cloudy third layer) may form between the top and bottom layers. Try not to disrupt the emulsion.</u>

FOR METHANOL, note that separate layers will not form.

2. Optional*: Pre-weigh second set of scintillation vials or other glass container with appropriate labels, including the isolate name, on analytical scale. Record weights.
3. Using a Pasteur pipette and bulb, transfer solvent from vials or containers in step 3 to pre-weighed vial or container. Follow specific instructions for solvent of choice below:

<u>FOR ETHYL ACETATE, transfer organic layer (top) – ethyl acetate with soluble components of the lawn and the agar – into pre-weighed vial or container. Carefully collect as much of the organic layer as possible. Avoid collecting emulsion (if present) and aqueous layer. It is better to leave some solvent than collect water. Once the organic layer is removed, keep vial or container uncapped in fume hood to evaporate remaining ethyl acetate. Afterwards, store aqueous phase at 4°C or freeze at -20°C if you intend to assay aqueous phase for activity (refer to note at the end of Session 4 Protocol).</u>

FOR METHANOL, transfer liquid – methanol with soluble components of the lawn and agar – into pre-weighed vial or container.

4. Allow extract to dry down by evaporation. Vials or containers with extracts may be left uncapped inside fume hood until next lab session, or until completely dried down. Alternatively, extracts may be dried using drying system or applied vacuum, which may reduce the drying-down period to several minutes or hours.

Note: Methanol retains water present in the agar and lawn and may therefore take longer to evaporate.

*Pre-weighing empty vials and containers prior to transferring extracts, and then re-weighing with dried extract, makes it possible to calculate how much extract is recovered from cultures. This facilitates preparing extracts at the same concentration, which makes it possible to compare the potency of different samples by assaying their activity based on a known concentration. Knowing the concentration of material facilitates using appropriate amounts of material in subsequent chemical analyses *via* Liquid Chromatography Mass Spectrometry or Thin Layer Chromatography (TLC). An analytical balance is highly recommended because the weight of extracted material can range from milligrams to submilligrams (less than 10^{-3} grams). It is advisable to keep the same vial and lid together since lids can vary substantially and a lid from a different extract can contaminate a sample.

SESSION 4 – ASSAY EXTRACT FOR ANTIBIOTIC ACTIVITY

Note: All dried extracts will be redissolved in methanol regardless of the solvent used in the extraction from Session 3.

MATERIALS
- Dried-down extract in scintillation vial or other glass container
- Media plates (same as isolate's original medium)
- Overnight culture of safe ESKAPE relative (your tester strain)
- Methanol
- Sterile 15-mL conical tube or test tube
- Micropipetteman and tips (P20 and P200)
- LB with 50% agar (top agar)

PROTOCOL
See Additional Safety Information above.***Note: LB with 0.75% agar (top agar) must be liquefied in microwave or water bath and allowed to cool down (warm to the touch) prior to step 8. If cooled too much, it will solidify.***

1. Your extracts are now dried down in a vial/container. If vials/containers were pre-weighed, re-weigh vial/container on the same analytical balance, calculate mass of dried extract, and record in your notes.
2. IF MASS NOT CALCULATED: Resuspend dried-extract in 80 µL methanol.

   OR

   IF MASS CALCULATED: Resuspend pre-weighed dried-extract methanol – adjust volume of solvent to attain desired concentration (recommended concentration: 5-10 µg/µL).
3. Prepare to spot the resuspended extract on a spread plate of safe ESKAPE relative (tester strain):

   Indicate on your media plate where extract and control will be spotted by drawing a dot on the back of the plate (one circle for each extract and one for the control).

   Note: Properly label back of media plate with safe ESKAPE relative name, isolate name, and extracts and controls to be spotted in the circles.

   Question: What will the control(s) be in the extract activity assay?

4. Using a P20 micropipetteman, spot 10 µL of resuspended extract on the appropriate pre-drawn dot (OR chosen volume if extract concentration is known; for example, you may want to use a

lower volume if extract is more concentrated). Allow the solvent to evaporate – the spot should appear dry. Repeat for methanol control.

5. Load another 10 µL (OR chosen volume) on same spot and let dry. Repeat for the control.

6. Repeat step 5 one more time until 30 µL total volume is loaded onto the appropriate pre-drawn dot.

7. While the spots are drying, obtain an overnight liquid culture of your tester strain and an empty, sterile conical tube or test tube. Set P200 micropipette to 100 µL.

Complete the following steps carefully but quickly to keep top agar from solidifying in the tube.

8. Using sterile technique, transfer 7 mL of liquefied top agar to the sterile tube. Alternatively, individual 7 mL aliquots of top agar can be prepared in advance in glass test tubes or 15 mL falcon tubes). Inoculate liquefied top agar in tube with 100 µL of tester strain overnight liquid culture.

9. Quickly and carefully pour inoculated top agar onto spotted media plate. Gently tilt the plate to spread top agar evenly over the entire plate. After covering entire surface, keep plate upright until top agar solidifies (i.e., becoming translucent and appearing more rigid).

10. Incubate at 28°C, or temperatures and conditions specific to isolate. Plate may be incubated upside-down after top agar solidifies. Incubate overnight or until tester strain grows into a lawn. Keep refrigerated at 4°C to avoid overgrowth until next lab session.

AQUEOUS PHASE NOTE: Session 4 Protocol may be repeated using aqueous phase. Note that aqueous spots will take significantly longer than those in organic solvents to evaporate in the fume hood and may not fully dry in one lab session. Alternatively, we recommend using a lyophilizer to dry down the frozen aqueous phase and then proceeding through Session 4 Protocol.

SESSION 5 – SCREEN ZONES OF INHIBITION

MATERIALS
- Plates from previous session

PROTOCOL
See Additional Safety Information above. Observe plates for zones of inhibition. Ensure that methanol control worked properly. Measure zones of inhibition and record observations. Did your organic extracts retain antibiotic activity? How do the zones of inhibition compare with observations made in previous assays?

Analyzing Sequences with BLAST Search

Note on protocol alternative below.

Genomes contain large amounts of information. The human genome is over 3 billion base pairs long, and bacterial genomes like *Escherichia coli* contain nearly 5 million base pairs. Making sense of all this information not only requires biological knowledge of how genes work and what they encode, but also powerful computational tools to sort through large amounts of information and solve problems. Sequenced genomes are submitted into large databases like GenBank that are impossible to navigate without search tools, just as Google Search helps us find specific information in the whole of the World Wide Web.

The Basic Local Alignment Search Tool (BLAST) (Altschul et al., 1990) is a bioinformatics tool that allows us to navigate through huge databases and compare an amino acid or nucleotide sequence with a library of published or submitted sequences. Using BLAST to compare DNA sequences allows us to find closely related genes or regions of DNA in the database. These closely related genes whose functions or organism of origin have been determined previously give us information about the likely function of a newly discovered gene's product or the identity of the organism from which it originated.

MATERIALS
- 16S rRNA gene* sequence and chromatogram
- BLAST website

*For more information on the 16S rRNA gene, please refer to Section 8 of the *Research Guide*.

PROTOCOL
1. Go to the BLAST website: http://www.ncbi.nlm.nih.gov/BLAST/.
2. Choose BLAST program to run a "Nucleotide BLAST."
3. Enter your sequence* into the "Enter Query Sequence" field and enter appropriate nucleotide range.*
4. Under "Choose Search Set," select the "16S ribosomal RNA sequences (Bacteria and Archaea)" database on the drop-down menu to conduct a search.
5. Once you have submitted your sequence and set the parameters, click "BLAST" at the bottom of the page. BLAST will take a couple of seconds to compare your sequence to other sequences in the database.
6. Once the search is done, analyze your BLAST data. The "Descriptions" column lists identifiers for similar sequences in the database. These identifiers are ranked by "Max Ident" (maximum identity), which is the percentage of matching nucleotides. Normally, a "Max Ident" of 97% or higher means that your sequence matches the specific description, which corresponds to a strain or species. The expected value (E value) tells you how statistically significant your match is; hence, the lower the E value, the more reliable the match.**

*Before entering your sequence into the "Enter Query Field," be sure to assess the quality of your sequence. This can be done by looking at your sequence trace chromatogram, which shows the fluorescence peaks given off by each of the four nucleotides during Sanger sequencing. You can view and trim sequence chromatograms using freely available software (e.g., Finch, DNA Baser, and 4Peaks). Peaks are considered low quality when they are not discrete or separated from one another; this usually happens at the beginning and end of the sequence. You can trim low-quality data from the beginning and end of the sequence or pick a "clean" nucleotide range in your sequence on which to conduct the BLAST analysis. After pasting your full sequence into the appropriate box, enter the appropriate region range into the "Query Subrange" fields.

**There are two numbers you should care about: Max score and E value. The higher the Max score, the better the match. The default BLAST algorithm assigns +2 for each matching nucleotide and -3 for each mismatch to give a raw score, and then it adjusts that score by length and database size to calculate the "Bit Score." The E value (or expected value) estimates how many times we expect to find a match of the same quality (bit score) in the database purely by chance. The lower the E value, the better. The matches with an E value above 1 can be discarded.

The Alignment – The first line with ">" gives the address (accession number) of the full entry in the database, name of the entry, and length. The summary section below the name shows the bit score and raw score in parentheses, E value, and % identity. The last part is the alignment itself: the query on top, the subject (sequence from the database) on the bottom, and vertical lines for each match between them. The numbers specify nucleotide position in each sequence.

NOTE ON PROTOCOL ALTERNATIVE: Students may also input their sequences into the RDP database (http://rdp.cme.msu.edu/seqmatch/seqmatch_intro.jsp), which specifically contains curated bacterial and archaeal 16S rRNA gene sequences.

REFERENCE

Altschul, S. F., Gish, W., Miller, W., Myers, E. W., & Lipman, D. J. (1990). Basic local alignment search tool. J Mol Biol, 215:403-410. doi: 10.1016/S0022-2836(05)80360-2.

Antibiotic Resistance Test

Note on protocol alternative below.

Soon after the introduction of antibiotics into clinical practice, resistant microorganisms were detected. Surprisingly, resistance to synthetic antibiotics (i.e., antibiotics created by chemists rather than found in Nature) appears as rapidly as resistance to natural antibiotics, proving incorrect predictions that because the synthetic antibiotics did not come from Nature, resistance had not yet evolved. Antibiotics that take great effort and money to develop for clinical use can become ineffective within months or years of their introduction – often due to drug misuse or overuse. The tendency of antibiotics to stop working has deterred pharmaceutical companies from pursuing new antibiotics even though the demand continues to rise. So, how does antibiotic resistance come about? We have noticed that, generally, low- and long-term exposure to antibiotics provides a selective pressure for microorganisms with favorable genotypes – those carrying resistance genes or with spontaneous mutations – to increase in frequency in the population (more on antibiotic resistance in Section 10). Selection pressure can result in the proliferation of resistant bacteria at the expense of sensitive ones of the same species, and the resistance genes can even be transferred to other species through horizontal gene transfer. This evolutionary phenomenon has existed for as long as antibiotics have existed in Nature; however, the incredibly fast rate at which antibiotic resistance spreads is associated with mass production and widespread use of antibiotics and is problematic.

Resistance varies in distribution and mechanism. Soil bacteria are resistant to their own antibiotics, often because of genes that confer resistance only to the antibiotic produced. Other resistance genes provide resistance to several antibiotics, and some bacteria contain many antibiotic resistance genes, making them resistant to many antibiotics. The soil antibiotic resistome is the collection of resistance genes from microorganisms in the soil. While humans have vastly increased the frequency of resistance genes in the bacterial world, resistant bacteria were present before antibiotic use by humans, and resistance genes can be found even in the most remote environments on the planet.

In this protocol, we will test bacterial isolates for the presence of resistance genes against common antibiotics. ***For more information on antibiotic resistance, please refer to Section 10 of the *Research Guide*.***

MATERIALS
- Antibiotic-containing media plates (See preparation for instructor below.)
- Sterile inoculating loops or toothpicks
- Streak plates of isolate to be tested or original master plate

Preparation of Antibiotic-Containing Media (for instructor)
1. Prepare LBA or isolate's original medium. Make enough media for each student to have one plate with medium of choice per antibiotic.
2. Place aliquots of media into separate capped bottles that will each be mixed with an aliquot of antibiotic solution. Placing the media into the bottles prior to autoclaving will decrease the chance of contamination. Alternatively, use aseptic technique to distribute the media after autoclaving.
3. After autoclaving media, allow to cool down (comfortably warm to the touch). Be sure to work quickly to keep the media from solidifying, or keep it warm in a water bath.
4. Follow antibiotic specifications in the table below for the following steps.
5. Determine the volume to antibiotic stock solution to be added to the batch of media.
6. Add x volume of antibiotic solution to batch of media, cap bottle, and mix gently by swirling to distribute antibiotic solution.

7. Pour plates and label appropriately. Keep plate containing light-sensitive antibiotics wrapped in foil or in the dark. After solidifying, store plates until lab session.

Antibiotic Specifications Chart

Antibiotic	Solvent	Stock solution and storage temperature	Working solution (final concentration)	Light sensitive?*	Antibiotic mode of action? *(to be completed by the student)*
Penicillin	Deionized (DI) water	10 mg/mL (-20°C)	10 µg/mL media	No	
Gramicidin	Methanol	10 mg/mL (-20°C)	10 µg/mL media	No	
Trimethoprim	Dimethyl sulfoxide (DMSO)	5 mg/mL (-20°C)	5 µg/mL media	No	
Rifampicin	DMSO	10 mg/mL (-20°C)	1 µg/mL media	Yes	
Tetracycline	70% ethanol	10 mg/mL (-20°C)	1 µg/mL media	Yes	

*Media with light-sensitive antibiotics must be wrapped in foil or stored in the dark. Plates must also be wrapped in foil or stored in the dark.

Note: Handle all solvents in a chemical fume hood. Ensure proper glove choice with use of DMSO since it can be absorbed directly into the skin. Label all secondary containers of chemicals and do not allow DMSO to enter drains. Dispose of chemical waste according to your institution's policies.

PROTOCOL

Note: Remember to use aseptic technique.

1. Obtain streak plates of your isolates (recommended) or original master plate.

2. Obtain antibiotic-containing media plate(s) of interest. Media plates will contain standard media (e.g., LB, PDA, and TSA) with the following antibiotic concentrations:
   a. Penicillin: 10 µg/mL
   b. Gramicidin: 10 µg/mL
   c. Trimethoprim: 5 µg/mL
   d. Rifampicin: 1 µg/mL
   e. Tetracycline: 1 µg/mL
3. Review Table 1 with antibiotic specifications. Ensure that antibiotic-containing media plate is labeled appropriately with antibiotic, concentration, and isolate(s) to be tested.
4. Using sterile inoculating loop or toothpick, pick isolate(s) from streak plate(s) or master plate and patch onto antibiotic plate. Make sure patch is labeled on the back of the plate with isolate name.
5. Incubate plate at isolate's designated growth conditions for 1-2 days, or until dense patch forms. If necessary, ensure plates are refrigerated at 4°C until next lab session to prevent overgrowth of patch (if next lab session does not meet for more than 2 days to make observations).
6. After incubation period, observe plates for growth. Does the isolate appear to be susceptible or resistant to the antibiotic? Develop a hypothesis that explains the result based on your observations and what you know about your isolate. Record observations.

NOTE ON PROTOCOL ALTERNATIVE: Instructor may use the Kirby-Bauer Disk Diffusion Susceptibility as an alternative to this protocol. This technique may be of interest to aspiring microbiologists. For more details on the Kirby-Bauer protocol and to see the procedure, please visit the ASM Microbe Library's Laboratory Protocols at http://www.asmscience.org/content/education/protocol/protocol.3189.

Catalase Test

Adapted from: Karen Reiner – Microbe Library

http://www.asmscience.org/content/education/protocol/protocol.3226

Hydrogen peroxide (H_2O_2) is a strong oxidizing agent that rapidly kills susceptible cells and is employed by many organisms to protect themselves against infectious bacteria. H_2O_2 is also used as an antiseptic applied on cuts or wounds on the skin; you will typically find it next to rubbing alcohol and first-aid kits at the store. Many bacteria have evolved defense mechanisms that allow them to counteract H_2O_2 activity in order to survive. This is facilitated by catalase, an enzyme that breaks down H_2O_2 into water and oxygen gas.

$$2H_2O_2 + \text{catalase} \rightarrow 2H_2O + O_2$$

Bacteria containing catalase will effervesce, or form bubbles of oxygen, when they come in contact with H_2O_2. This serves as a simple test for the presence of catalase. For this reason, it was one of the bacterial enzymes described and used to classify bacteria (Gagnon et al., 1959; McLeod et al., 1923). A 3% H_2O_2 solution is typically used to test bacteria for catalase activity. Other applications, especially in diagnostics, include the identification of anaerobes using 15% H_2O_2 solution, as anaerobes typically lack the enzyme (Bartelt, 2000).

MATERIALS

- 3% H_2O_2
- glass microscope slides or Petri dishes
- inoculating loop or toothpicks
- streak plates of isolates
- streak plates of positive and negative controls (from safe ESKAPE relatives: Positive: *P. putida*; Negative: *S. epidermidis*)

PROTOCOL

1. Obtain the streak plate of your bacterial isolate with fresh (1-3-day-old), fully grown colonies.
2. Obtain a microscope slide. Optional: Place microscope slide inside a Petri dish and cover with lid to limit catalase aerosols during the test.
3. Using a sterile inoculating loop, stick, or toothpick, pick a single colony from the streak plate. A small yet visible amount of cells will suffice. Note: Avoid picking up agar with the bacterial cells as the agar, especially if it containing red blood cells, can lead to a false-positive reaction.
4. Gently apply the cells with a back-and-forth motion until there is a small, visible smear in the center of the slide. To conserve materials, smear up to three isolates in separate smears on a single slide.
5. Using dropper or pipette, place 1 drop of 3% H_2O_2 solution onto the smear on the slide. Do not mix. Note: Carrying out steps 5 and 6 on a dark background will enhance the visibility of bubbles.
6. Observe for the production of oxygen bubbles – this will happen rapidly and vigorously in a positive reaction. A weak reaction or no reaction may indicate a negative. Optional: For weak catalase-positive microorganisms, examine slides under a dissecting microscope or using 4x or 10x magnification on a light microscope.
7. Perform a control reaction using organisms known to be positive and negative for catalase.

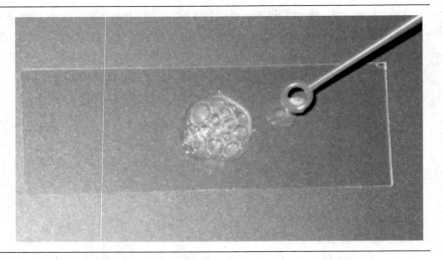

Figure 2. Slide of catalase test results. This positive reaction was produced by *Staphylococcus aureus*.
Photo from commons.wikimedia.org.

REFERENCES

Bartelt, M. (2000). Diagnostic Bacteriology, a Study Guide. Philadelphia, PA: F. A. Davis Co.

Gagnon, M., Hunting, W., & Esselen, W. B. (1959). A new method for catalase determination. Anal Chem, 31:144.

McLeod, J. W., & Gordon, J. (1923). Catalase production and sensitiveness to hydrogen peroxide amongst bacteria: with a scheme for classification based on these properties. J Pathol Bacteriol, 26:326-331.

Adapted from:

Reiner, K. (2010). "Catalase Test Protocol." Laboratory Protocols. **Microbe Library**. *American Society for Microbiology*. Accessed 13 October 2013.
<<http://www.asmscience.org/content/education/protocol/protocol.3226>>

Colony Morphology

Since bacteria were first cultured on solid media, microbiologists have noticed that colonies display differences in physical appearance at the macroscopic level, just like organisms are distinguishable from one another based on how they look. Reference books such as *Bergey's Manual of Systematic Bacteriology* contain extensive descriptions of bacterial physical and functional attributes, which have enabled microbiologists to identify and classify bacteria for nearly a century. Colony morphology is one of the first things we observe about bacteria at the macroscale and use to distinguish them from other microbes and distantly related bacteria. The main descriptors used by microbiologists are: (1) color, (2) surface texture and elevation, (3) shape, and (4) margin. We use specific terms to describe morphological characteristics, such the ones described in Figure 3. However, bacteria come in many forms; therefore, there is much room for creativity when describing colony morphology.

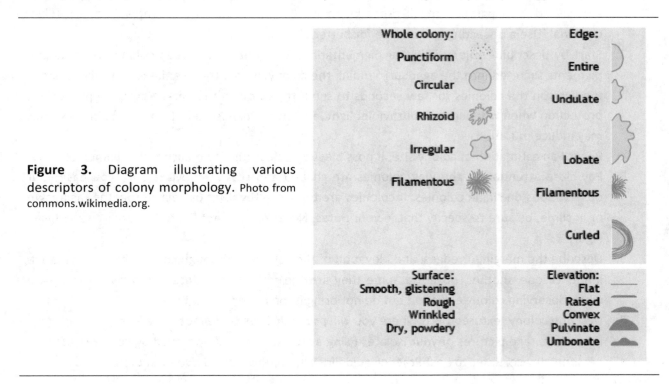

Figure 3. Diagram illustrating various descriptors of colony morphology. Photo from commons.wikimedia.org.

PROTOCOL

1. Allow streak plate of bacterial isolates or master plate to grow for 2-4 days at optimal growth conditions. **Note:** Even if colonies are visible after a one-day incubation period, give the cells more time to produce pigments and other morphological identifiers that may not be as evident at the logarithmic growth phase, when colonies are still growing.

2. Once your cells are in the stationary phase of growth, start observing and describing their physical characteristics. **Note:** Keep the plate covered whenever possible, and keep it covered and sealed with parafilm at all times when working with unknown isolates in a BSL-1 lab. **Optional:** Use a dissecting microscope for better observations.

3. Start by describing colony color, or pigmentation. Differentiate between colony pigments and pigments secreted into the agar surrounding the colony. If an ultraviolet lamp is available, shine the light on the colonies for few seconds to see if they glow in the dark. **Note:** Use proper eye protection when working with ultraviolet light, and do not expose cells for too long because this may induce mutations.

4. Record an estimation of colony size; if possible, use a clear ruler to measure the diameter.

5. Pay close attention to the way colonies are shaped and scattered. Make sure you base your observations on single colonies. If colonies are too close together or packed together as a lawn or in slime, be sure to specify that in your notes. **Note:** You are not limited to using the terms in Figure 3.

6. Describe the margin, or edges, and elevation of the colonies. Although colony shape and margin influence one another, do not assume they are the same thing. **Note:** Carefully tilt the plate when observing colony elevation but do not bring it too close to your face.

7. Describe colony texture; this is where you will probably have to be most creative.

8. If possible, take pictures of your isolates using a lab camera or, if approved by your instructor, a personal device. Refer to Best Practice guidelines in the *Research Guide* for more details.

Colony PCR

Polymerase chain reaction (PCR) is a common technique used to **amplify** (make multiple copies of) specific regions of DNA for applications, including sequencing and genetic analysis. PCR helps scientists overcome the problem of having too little material or an impure DNA sample to study. Developed in 1983 by the biochemist Kary Mullis, this elegant technique uses the same mechanism cells use to make copies of their genetic material during reproduction, except PCR does it without the cells themselves. PCR is carried out in a test tube containing the DNA template we wish to study, primers, DNA polymerase, and reagents that stabilize the reaction in water. Each round of PCR requires three steps: (1) denaturation, (2) annealing, and (3) elongation, each of which doubles the amount of DNA template present in the reaction.

The **DNA template** can be any DNA molecule, such as a bacterial chromosome, a plasmid, or a fragment of DNA. We use **primers** to specify which region of DNA in the template we wish to amplify. A primer is a short fragment of single-stranded DNA (ssDNA), which binds (or anneals) to one strand of the DNA template and is recognized by the enzyme **DNA polymerase** as the starting point of the reaction. In the first step of the reaction (**denaturation**), our double-stranded DNA (dsDNA) template must be "unzipped" into two separate strands. To denature dsDNA, we must disrupt the hydrogen bonds between complementary base pairs by raising the reaction temperature to 94°C. In the second step (**annealing**), the temperature is lowered to 58°C, allowing the ssDNA template and primers to bind at the specific sites. There are typically two primers, one for each complementary strand. In the third step (**elongation**), DNA polymerase recognizes the primer and starts synthesizing a new complementary DNA strand in the 5' to 3' direction.

Repeating this process over multiple rounds, typically around 30, allows us to amplify DNA exponentially. However, this means that we must work with a highly stable enzyme that will withstand great fluctuations in temperature without compromising its structure and function or the quality of the new DNA copies. Just as dsDNA denatures at high temperatures, so do enzymes. Most enzymes irreversibly lose their three-dimensional structure and activity at very high temperatures. In the past, scientists needed to add new enzymes in every round of the reaction, decreasing the efficiency and the reliability of PCR by building up a massive protein concentration through successive rounds of amplification. An extreme bacterium, *Thermus aquaticus*, a thermophilic or "heat-loving" bacterium isolated from the hot springs of the Yellowstone National Park, held the answer to this problem. This microorganism could survive and reproduce at near-boiling temperatures, which also indicated that its enzymes were heat-resistant as well. A team was able to purify *Thermus aquaticus*' DNA polymerase, or Taq polymerase for short. This enzyme has an optimal temperature of 72°C, whereas most enzymes used in molecular biology work optimally at 37°C. Taq polymerase has become the standard enzyme used in PCR (Saiki et al., 1988), revolutionizing our ability to amplify and study DNA with high fidelity.

PCR Bead Method

MATERIALS
- 27F primer (stock solution: 20 µM)*
- 1492R primer (stock solution: 20 µM)*
- llustra™ PuReTaq™ Ready-To-Go™ PCR Bead and tube
- Sterile nuclease-free deionized water (ultrapure)
- Streak plate of isolate
- Micropipettemen and tips
- Optional: Heat block

*Stored at -20°C

PROTOCOL
Protocol adapted from "puReTaq Ready-To-Go PCR Beads" guide.

1. Obtain PCR bead tubes, which contain Taq polymerase (heat-resistant enzyme) and other necessary reagents. Label tubes with names of isolates or DNA samples, and if possible, primers used.
2. Dispense 23 µL of ultrapure water into the PCR bead tube. The bead will start to dissolve and slightly effervesce. Optional: Use the heat block to preheat primer stocks to 80°C for 2 minutes and plunge in ice prior to adding to reaction mix.
3. Add 1 µL of forward primer (27F). As you dispense the primer solution, insert the micropipette tip into the mix so that the small volume goes directly into the mix.
4. Add 1 µL of reverse primer (1492R) to the mix. This will bring the volume of the reaction mix to 25 µL.
5. Using a micropipette tip, carefully touch the colony on the streak plate. A small, visible dab of cell that barely fills the very end of the pipette tip will provide enough DNA template for the reaction. Optional: Resuspend cells in 100 µL of 1x phosphate-buffer saline (PBS) solution, mix thoroughly by gently vortexing, and add 5 µL of the cell suspension to the mix. This will bring the reaction mix volume to 30 µL.
6. Dip pipette tip into reaction mix and gently swirl for 5-10 seconds to dislodge cells. Cap the tubes. If necessary, gently tap for a few seconds to attain a more uniform mix and collect all of the reagents at the bottom of the tube. Avoid forming bubbles.
7. Transfer tubes to thermal cycler (PCR machine).
8. Select appropriate program† to start cycling (about 2 hours).
9. Once cycling is complete, remove tubes and incubate on ice. Follow your instructor's instructions about storage and follow-up protocols to quality test the PCR products and prepare them for sequencing.

Reagent Method

MATERIALS

- Master mix = primers, buffer, dNTPs, $MgCl_2$, H_2O, and DNA polymerase
    - 0.1-0.5 µM (final concentration) forward primer
    - 0.1-0.5 µM (final concentration) reverse primer
    - Polymerase buffer (1x final concentration) (may be provided with polymerase)
    - 0.2 mM each dNTP (final concentration)
    - 1.5-2.5 mM (final concentration) $MgCl_2$
    - DNA polymerase (e.g., Taq) (adjust concentration depending on product specifications)
- H_2O to 25-100 µL final volume
- Template DNA = small pin-head volume of bacterial cells OR 5 µL of cell suspension.

Optional: Make a cell suspension by resuspending cells in 100 µL of phosphate-buffer saline (PBS) solution and mix thoroughly by vortexing gently.

PROTOCOL

1. Obtain all PCR reagents except enzyme (keep frozen). Thaw on ice. Label tubes with names of isolates or DNA samples and, if possible, primers used. Place on ice.
2. Determine the volume of each reagent to add to your reaction(s) and calculate amounts for master mix if appropriate.
3. Add each reagent to master mix starting with water and ending with the DNA polymerase enzyme. Add everything but the template (bacterial cells or cell lysis) to your master mix; check off as added. Put Taq enzyme back in freezer.
4. Dispense master mix into individual tubes.
5. Using a micropipette tip, carefully touch the colony on the streak plate. A small dab that collects a small yet visible blob of cells will provide enough DNA template for the reaction. Or, add 5 µL of the cell suspension to the mix.
6. Using a micropipetteman, mix the contents of each tube by gently swishing the solution up and down several times. Cap the tubes. If necessary, gently flick or vortex for a few seconds to attain a more uniform mix.
7. Transfer tubes to thermal cycler (PCR machine).
8. Select appropriate program† to start cycling (about 2 hours).
9. Once cycling is complete, remove tubes and keep in ice. Follow your instructor's directions about storage and follow-up protocols to quality test the PCR products and prepare them for sequencing.

†PCR cycling program:

94°C for 10 minutes – breaking down cells/ denaturation
94°C for 30 seconds – denaturation
58°C 30 seconds – annealing
72°C 1 min 50 sec (1 minute per kb of DNA template) – elongation
Cycle 30 times
72°C for 10 minutes

REFERENCES

Saiki, R. K., Gelfand, D. H., Stoffel, S., Scharf, S. J., Higuchi, R., Horn, G. T., Mullis, K. B., & Erlich, H. A. (1988). Primer-directed enzymatic amplification of DNA with a thermostable DNA polymerase. Science, 239:487-491.

Fermentation

Adapted from: Clifford Grimsley – Gaston College

Many organic compounds can be produced through fermentation, and many microbes satisfy their energy requirements through fermentation in which carbohydrates are incompletely oxidized because oxygen is insufficient. This incomplete oxidation produces several different end products, such as acids, alcohols, aldehydes, and gases, such as methane or CO_2. Microbes ferment different substances and produce diverse end products, which are also characteristic of taxonomic groups; thus, both the substrates and end products of fermentation are characteristic of taxonomic groups, making fermentation capabilities extraordinarily useful in microbe identification.

Fermentation of carbohydrates often results in the production of acid and gas. To determine whether an acid is produced, a pH indicator can be added to the growth medium. Growth media containing the pH indicator Phenol Red are normally red or pink at a pH 7, and a change to yellow indicates acid is produced. The production of gas is observed by using a Durham tube, which is an ordinary test tube that contains a small inverted vial. If gas is produced, the inverted vial will collect some of the gas, and a bubble will be visible. The fermentation media are prepared by adding 0.05% of a single carbohydrate and 0.02% of a pH indicator to a nutrient broth medium. If the organism can break down the particular carbohydrate in the tube, then the various end products will be produced.

MATERIALS
- Durham fermentation tube containing lactose + phenol red
- Durham fermentation tube containing dextrose + phenol red
- Durham fermentation tube containing sucrose + phenol red
- Streak plates of isolates

- Streak plates of positive and negative controls (*Bacillus subtilis, Escherichia coli, Proteus vulgaris, Staphylococcus epidermidis,* and *Serratia marcescens*)

PROTOCOL

1. Pick bacterial isolate with a stick or inoculating loop. Inoculate the three carbohydrate broths with your isolate. Repeat for each isolate and control.
2. Be sure that each tube is labeled with the carbohydrate and the inoculated organism. Place the tubes in a beaker labeled with the initials of your group and the date.
3. Incubate all tubes at the appropriate temperature (25°C for most of our environmental isolates) for 24-48 hours.
4. Your instructor may set up additional controls for you to view.
5. After the incubation, compare each of the inoculated tubes with the control tube of the same media to determine whether acid or gas was produced. Record your results.

Fermentation Protocol Data Sheet

Carbohydrates	*S. marcescens*	*E. coli*	*S. epidermidis*	*B. subtilis*	*P. vulgaris*
Dextrose					
Lactose					
Sucrose					

Note: Ensure non-pathogenic *E. coli* strains are chosen for these experiments.

Record results as follows:

AG = Acid and gas produced
A= Acid only produced
a = Slight acidity produced
O = Carbohydrate not fermented

Gram Stain

Excerpt from *Research Guide* (Section 8):

Developed in the late 1800s, Gram stain is one of the most famous classical methods to help visualize bacteria in biopsies and has become critical to the taxonomic classification of bacteria. Staining allows us to enhance our ability to see the shape of the bacterial cell and helps us distinguish the two main patterns of cell wall architecture. It does this by binding to cellular components that would otherwise be transparent under the light microscope. Bacterial cell walls are composed of a meshwork of polymers of proteins, lipids, and sugars, which serve as signatures for classifying bacteria. The bacterial cell wall consists of highly cross-linked polymers of sugar and amino acids called peptidoglycan. The peptidoglycan layer protects bacteria and gives cells their characteristic shapes.

Gram stain employs two stains, crystal violet and safranin, which are violet and red, respectively. In Gram-positive bacteria, the peptidoglycan layer is very thick (>20 nanometers) and exposed to the outside. Gram-positive cells retain large amounts of crystal violet in this layer, and binding is fixed with a mordant, iodine, giving the cells a purple appearance under the microscope even after washing cells with a decolorizer, such as alcohol. Conversely, in Gram-negative bacteria, the peptidoglycan layer is thin (normally <10 nanometers) and covered by an outer membrane, the S-layer. It retains very little crystal violet but stains well with the counterstain safranin, which gives the cells a pink appearance under the microscope. By discriminating between purple and pink cells on a microscope slide, clinical microbiologists can deduce much information about an isolate's physiology. Furthermore, Gram staining serves as a classification system for bacteria. Gram-positives and Gram-negatives make up two major subdivisions of bacteria, which are generally representative of different taxonomic groups. Therefore, Gram stain, as a classical method, is still widely used to differentiate bacteria, and clinical personnel and microbiologists use it as a preliminary method of characterization.

In addition, Gram stain or other staining methods provide contrast to assist in observation of the shape of the bacterial cell. Negative staining with nigrosin is also used to determine cell shape. Bacteria come in many shapes, but the most commonly observed are spherical [called cocci (plural) or coccus (singular)] and rod-shaped [called bacilli (plural) or bacillus (singular)].

Atypical Gram Stain

Adapted from: Ann C. Smith, Marise A. Hussey – Microbe Library

<http://www.asmscience.org/content/education/protocol/protocol.2886>

Some bacteria, after staining with the Gram stain yield a pattern called Gram-variable where a mix of pink and purple cells is observed. The genera *Actinomyces, Arthrobacter, Corynebacterium, Mycobacterium,* and *Propionibacterium* have cell walls that are particularly sensitive to breakage during cell division, resulting in Gram-negative staining of these Gram-positive cells. In cultures of *Bacillus,*

Butyrivibrio, and *Clostridium,* a decrease in peptidoglycan thickness during growth coincides with an increasing number cells that stain Gram-negative (Beveridge, 1990). In addition, in all bacteria stained using the Gram stain, the age of the culture may influence the results of the stain. Older and denser cultures of *Bacillus* and *Clostridium*, for example, tend to form endospores, which look like pink ovals with little staining in the center of the cell.

Note: Some bacteria are known to give unexpected or inconclusive results from the Gram stain. For example, *Acinetobacter* spp., like our ESKAPE safe relative *Acinetobacter baylyi*, are Gram-negative cocci and are more resistant to the decolorization step. Thus, these cells can often appear Gram-positive even if the steps are performed perfectly. *Mycobacterium* spp., while Gram-positive bacteria, have a unique waxy peptidoglycan composed of mycolic acids that is difficult to stain with the dyes used in the Gram stain protocol. Misinterpretations of the Gram stain have led to mis- or delayed diagnosis of infectious disease (Visca et al., 2001; Noviello et al., 2004).

Figure 4. [Left] *Bacillus subtilis*, a Gram-positive bacterium, stained purple with crystal violet. **[Right]** *Citrobacter freundii*, a Gram-negative bacterium, stained reddish/pink with counterstain safranin. Photos from commons.wikimedia.org.

MATERIALS

- Gram stain kit
- Isolate streak plate or master plate (1- to 3-day-old culture or fresh culture stored at 4°C)
- Positive and negative controls
- Inoculating loop, stick, or toothpick
- Microscope slide
- Forceps
- Sink or tray
- Paper towel
- Bright-field microscope and immersion oil
- Optional: Hot plate or slide warmer (could be used instead of a Bunsen burner or flame)

PROTOCOL

1. Draw three evenly separated circles on a clean, dry microscope slide and label outside with bacterial isolate designation. Place a small drop of water in the circle.
2. Collect a small sample of bacterial colony with the tip of a stick/toothpick or inoculating loop.
3. Disperse the bacterial sample from the stick/toothpick or inoculating loop within the center drop of water. Let dry. Repeat for controls on each side for comparison. You can use the ESKAPE safe relatives for controls. (i.e., Gram-positive: *Staphylococcus epidermidis, Bacillus subtilis, Enterococcus raffinosus*; Gram-negative: *Pseudomonas putida, Erwinia carotovora, Acinetobacter baylyi*).
4. Using forceps, fix cells by passing slide through the Bunsen burner flame 3 or 4 times with the smear facing up. Optional: Heat fix cells by putting slide on hot plate (set to warm or low heat) for 1-2 minutes. Note: Heat fixing a wet sample will cause cells to boil and disrupt their cell walls and will negatively affect stain results.
5. Transfer slide to a sink or a tray where stains can be rinsed. Carefully hold one end of the slide with forceps or gloved hands. If staining multiple slides, mount the slides on a wire rack or any other surface that will allow rinsing to flow through.
6. Flood smear with crystal violet for 1 minute.
7. Gently rinse slide with an indirect stream of water from the tab or a squirt bottle for about 2 seconds. Note: Slightly tilt slide and gently dispense water over the smear, not directly onto the smear. Blot the edges of the slide on paper towel being careful not to wipe the smear.
8. Flood smear with Gram iodine. Wait 1 minute.
9. As in step 7, gently rinse with water and blot edges of the slide on paper towel.
10. Drip 95% alcohol solution across the smear for less than 15 seconds and until the solution runs clear off the smear. Do a quick rinse with water. Quickly blot on paper towel. Note: This is a critical step in Gram staining. Too much decolorizing agent for too long will lead to erroneous results. Note: You may use 75% ethanol and 25% acetone as an alternative decolorizer.
11. Flood smear with safranin for 1 minute.
12. Gently rinse with water and blot.
13. Let slide air-dry for several minutes.
14. View slide under the microscope under bright field. Use oil immersion for greater magnification.

REFERENCES

Beveridge, T.J. (1990). Mechanism of Gram variability in select bacteria. J. Bacteriol, 172:1609-1620.

Noviello, S., Gallo, R., Kelly, M., Limberger, R. J., DeAngelis, K., Cain, L. et al. (2004). Laboratory-acquired brucellosis. Emerging Infectious Diseases, 10:1848-1850.
<http://wwwnc.cdc.gov/eid/article/10/10/04-0076_article>

Visca, P., Petrucca, A., De Mori, P., Festa, A., Boomis, E., Antinori, A., & Petrosillo, N. (2001). Community-acquired *Acinetobacter radioresistens* bacteremia in an HIV-positive patient. Emerging Infectious Diseases, 7:1032-1035.
<https://wwwnc.cdc.gov/eid/article/7/6/01-0621_article>

Adapted from:

Smith, A. C., & Hussey, M. A. (2005). "Gram Stain Protocols." Laboratory Protocols. **Microbe Library**. *American Society for Microbiology*. Accessed 13 October 2013. <http://www.asmscience.org/content/education/protocol/protocol.2886>

MacConkey Agar Test

Excerpt from *Research Guide* (Section 11):

MacConkey agar is a specialized medium utilized to differentiate among Gram-negative bacteria, especially those that inhabit the human gastrointestinal (GI) tract. This medium inhibits the growth of Gram-positive bacteria by disrupting their cell walls with crystal violet and bile salts infused in the medium. Many Gram-negative bacteria, such as *Escherichia coli*, thrive in the GI tract as part of our natural gut flora along with many specialized Gram-positive bacteria. Other Gram-negative bacteria, including *Salmonella* and *Shigella* are notorious pathogens that can cause food poisoning and even death. To differentiate among these bacteria, MacConkey agar allows us to deduce information about their ability to ferment carbohydrates. A pH indicator in the medium changes the appearance of cells producing acid as a by-product of fermentation from their original color to pink/red. *Escherichia coli* ferments the lactose present in the medium and releases acid, making colonies and the surrounding agar appear red in the presence of a pH indicator. Conversely, *Salmonella* and *Shigella* do not ferment lactose and maintain a neutral pH, making colonies display their typical white or tan color (Wessner, Dupont, & Charles, p. 176). MacConkey agar is therefore both selective and differential, telling us about the cell wall composition and the cell's ability to ferment lactose.

Differentiating Bacteria with the MacConkey Agar Test

Adapted from: Mary E. Allen – Microbe Library

<http://www.asmscience.org/content/education/protocol/protocol.2855>

MacConkey agar is a specialized bacterial medium that can be used to differentiate Gram-negative bacteria for their ability to ferment lactose. The addition of crystal violet and bile salts to the medium selects against the growth of both Gram-positive and fastidious Gram-negative bacteria. Most Gram-negative bacteria can tolerate bile salts due to their protective outer membrane. For these reasons, MacConkey agar is commonly used to isolate enteric bacteria from water, food, and biological samples.

MACCONKEY AGAR RECIPE

Peptone (Difco) or Gelysate (BBL)	17 g
Proteose peptone (Difco) or Polypeptone (BBL)	3.0 g
Lactose	10 g
NaCl	5.0 g
Crystal Violet	1.0 mg
Neutral Red	30 mg
Bile Salts	1.5 g
Agar	13 g
Distilled Water	Add to make 1 L

Adjust pH to 7.1 ± 0.2. Boil to dissolve agar. Sterilize at 121°C for 15 minutes.

PROTOCOL

1. Streak a plate of MacConkey agar with your isolate of interest.
2. Streak plate of *Escherichia coli* or other Gram-negative control from ESKAPE safe relatives on MacConkey agar. Strains that ferment lactose (such as *E. coli*) will appear red/pink after growth. Strains that do not ferment lactose appear colorless and translucent.

REFERENCE

Wessner, D. R., Dupont, C., & Charles, T. (2013). Microbiology.

Adapted from:

Allen, M. E. (2005). "MacConkey Agar Plates Protocols." Laboratory Protocols. **Microbe Library**. *American Society for Microbiology*. Accessed 13 October 2013. <http://www.asmscience.org/content/education/protocol/protocol.2855>

Making Glycerol Stocks

When working with bacterial isolates in multiple experiments, it is important to preserve and store bacteria in an unchanging state where cells can be accessed for future use. Freezing allows us to keep bacteria in a dormant state for long periods of time, with one disadvantage – water forms ice crystals upon freezing, which can rupture and kill cells. To keep this from happening, we freeze bacteria in a glycerol solution, which bathes and stabilizes bacterial cells by preventing the formation of ice crystals. Bacteria and bacterial spores can be stored for years at -80°C in 20% glycerol solution and liquid medium.

MATERIALS
- 80% glycerol solution
- Fresh streak plate
- Liquid medium (same as streak plate)
- Cryogenic vials (1.5 or 1.8 mL)

PROTOCOL

1. Streak out bacterial isolate on appropriate medium. Incubate until colonies are visible.
2. Premix 80% glycerol and liquid medium in a conical tube. Adjust to a final concentration of 20% glycerol with liquid medium. (Note: if your isolate is streaked on LB agar, mix glycerol with LB broth.)
3. Dispense 1000-1200 µL of 20% glycerol mix into cryogenic vial. Label tube with isolate designation, glycerol concentration, and date. For example: SH-LB-1, 20% gly, 11/12/13. Use an alcohol-proof and waterproof marker.
4. Using a sterile inoculating loop, pick a single colony from the streak plate. Collect as much of the colony as possible without picking up agar.
5. Carefully pick the inoculating loop off the plate and quickly transfer it to the respectively labeled cryogenic vial. Insert loop into the glycerol mix and gently wiggle or twist the handle to deposit the colony in the glycerol mix. ***Note: Whenever possible, keep the vial supported in a rack, and if picked up for observation, keep below eye level and pointed away from your body.
6. Gently pipette up and down or gently vortex the cryogenic vial until the colony is uniformly mixed.
7. Freeze and store glycerol stock at -80°C.
8. Input the bacterial isolate information and location of glycerol stock in your notes and in the Small World Initiative Soil Sample Database.

Methanol Extraction

In the "Analyzing Organic Extracts for Antibiotic Production" protocol, we used ethyl acetate to extract secondary metabolites from isolates. It is important to realize, however, that ethyl acetate is just one of many organic solvents that can be used in extractions. Each solvent will extract a different set of compounds based on the solvent's and the compounds' chemical characteristics.

Methanol is commonly used in extractions. While ethyl acetate is relatively nonpolar, methanol is one of the most polar organic solvents. On the one hand, its polarity means that a wide range of compounds will be soluble in methanol. As a result, methanol extractions tend to capture a greater number and variety of organic compounds. On the other hand, using a strong polar solvent like methanol also has disadvantages. Because methanol and water have similar polarities, methanol is miscible in water, meaning that the two liquids will form a homogenous mixture. Therefore, extractions using methanol will not result in distinct and separable organic and aqueous fractions, but rather they result in a single layer that contains both water (from the agar) and methanol. A drawback of this solvent-water mixture is that it evaporates far more slowly than solvent alone, meaning that the drying process for methanol extractions can be long and tedious.

MATERIALS
- Methanol
- Glass Pasteur pipettes
- Scintillation vials

PROTOCOL

Additional Safety Information
Warning: All chemical solvents should be handled in a chemical fume hood to avoid inhalation, which can cause adverse health effects. **Ensure flammable solvents (e.g., ethanol and methanol) do not come into contact with flames or ignition sources.**

1. Follow the procedure described in "Day 1" and "Day 2" of the "Analyzing Organic Extracts for Antibiotic Production" protocol. The result should be glass bottles containing frozen samples of chopped agar and isolate lawns.
2. Add 20 mL of methanol to bottle of frozen sample and place on a shaker for ~1 hour or overnight.
3. Pre-weigh scintillation vials. Record weights in table.
4. Carefully remove all liquid from the bottle with a glass Pasteur pipette and transfer to a clean, weighed scintillation vial.
5. Label vial appropriately.

6. Hand vials and table of vial weights to instructor. The instructor will dry these extracts using a nitrogen dryer. (Note: It may take several days for these extracts to dry completely.)
7. Once extracts are dry, resuspend material in 80 µL methanol and follow the procedure described in "Day 4" of the "Analyzing Organic Extracts for Antibiotic Production" protocol to assay the samples for bioactivity.

EXTRACTIONS USING OTHER SOLVENTS

Some other common solvents can be used to extract compounds by making slight alterations to the original "Analyzing Organic Extracts for Antibiotic Production" protocol:

2-butanol:

Although 2-butanol is immiscible in water, the organic and aqueous fractions are typically not as distinct as when ethyl acetate is used. The cloudy region in between these layers can be eliminated using centrifugation. Transfer the liquid to a conical tube and centrifuge for 5 minutes at 10,000 rpm. The organic layer can then be easily pipetted to a scintillation vial for drying.

Hexane:

Hexane is easy to use for extractions because it evaporates quickly. However, when hexane is spotted onto agar, it spreads across the plate quite far from the point where it was originally spotted. Therefore, if hexane is used as the extraction solvent, the bioassay procedure must be altered. Rather than spotting 10 µL of resuspended extract 3 times (as described in "Day 4"), spot 5 µL of resuspended hexane extract 6 times.

Obtaining Soil Sample

Soil harbors an abundance of microbial biodiversity, coming in different forms and different packages. Studies of soil samples across the planet show that even the most remote and extreme environments are rich in microbial life. Even our local and familiar soils are rich and dynamic, and they remain largely unchartered in the laboratory. The goal in this protocol is to demonstrate just how "exotic" local soil environments can be and how much we can learn and discover from them. Your task is to choose an ecosystem and bring back a soil sample to study in the laboratory. Pick a sample that encapsulates a good representation of your ecosystem of choice and that is rich in biodiversity.

MATERIALS
- Container: conical tube or sandwich bag
- Soil collection worksheet (paper or electronic)

PROTOCOL

Additional Safety Information
Note: At the completion of work, soil samples should be autoclaved prior to disposal out of an abundance of caution. Your biosafety officer may require records on the autoclave run and the date of sample destruction, which should be maintained in your records.

1. Define what biodiversity means to you and write down what indicates that an ecosystem or soil environment is rich in biodiversity.
2. Write down a set of criteria for picking a soil sample and choose what location(s) you wish to study. Note: Only collect soil samples from the state in which your institution is located to avoid issues with interstate movement of soils, which require USDA APHIS permits. Additional legal requirements exist for foreign samples, including those related to protection of natural resources, ownership, and movement of biodiversity and pathogens.
3. Obtain 1 or 2 containers to collect a soil sample and a soil collection worksheet.
4. Go out into the environment and collect a small soil sample – pick 5-10 g of soil or roughly a handful of soil.
   a. For conical tube, take the lid off and use the open tube to scoop soil directly.
   b. For sandwich bag, turn the bag inside out, grab a fistful of soil, and wrap bag around soil.
5. Close your container and keep until next lab session. Try to keep cool and away from the sun.
6. Fill in your soil collection worksheet with information about your soil sample: location, date and time, weather conditions, habitat, surrounding plant and animal life, and other descriptive information. For location and weather, feel free to use maps or a weather app to get an estimate.
7. Develop hypotheses about your soil sample. What do you speculate you will learn or discover from your soil sample? How does that match your original set of criteria?

Soil Sample Data Collection Sheet – Location & Site Conditions

Adapted from: Kristen Butela – Seton Hill University

Worksheet also available in Research Protocols. **Include your data in the Small World Initiative Soil Sample Database:** *www.smallworldinitiative.org/data*

*Collected By:	
*General Location:	
GPS Coordinates via Google Earth (e.g., Latitude, Longitude):	
*Date & Time Collected:	
*Sample Site Descriptors:	
Air Temperature (°C):	
Humidity (%):	
Depth (In.):	
Type of Soil:	
Soil Temperature (°C):	
pH of Soil:	
Soil Water Content (%):	
Additional Data to be Determined in Lab (Weather Conditions, Organic Content):	

* Indicates field is required in the Small World Initiative Soil Sample Database.

Additional Documentation:

- Photo of sample site
- List of any plant species present near site
- Photo of soil in collection tube

Soil Sampling Kit Contents:

- Data sheets
- 50-mL conical tubes
- Lab marker
- "Scientific Soil Sample Collection Device" (plastic knife or spoon)
- Alcohol pads (used to disinfect collection device, thermometer, and ruler in between samplings)
- Thermometer
- Site marking flag (if return to site necessary)
- Plastic ruler

Printout of "Guide of Texture by Feel":

<https://www.nrcs.usda.gov/wps/portal/nrcs/detail/soils/edu/kthru6/?cid=nrcs142p2_054311>

Picking and Patching Colonies

Isolating single species of bacteria from a mixed culture containing tens or hundreds of species is a routine procedure that allows microbiologists to carefully examine an organism and its unique characteristics. Dilution plating allows us to spread individual bacteria on a plate to grow into distinct colonies. Yet, colonies overgrow with time and mix with one another, cells migrate, and cultures get contaminated, so sterile conditions in your work environment and proper techniques are very important to isolating a bacterium and starting a pure culture.

The isolation approach we will use is aptly called "pick and patch" and involves precisely those things: "picking" bacteria from a mixed culture (e.g., usually a dilution plate) and "patching" them onto a fresh plate, which may be a pure culture or a "master plate" containing all your unique bacteria of interest for your study. The light touch of a colony with a sterile toothpick or a metal rod picks up thousands of bacteria that can be transferred and smeared or patched onto a fresh plate. At the end of this procedure, you will have a "master plate" that will serve as a bacterial catalog for your experiments.

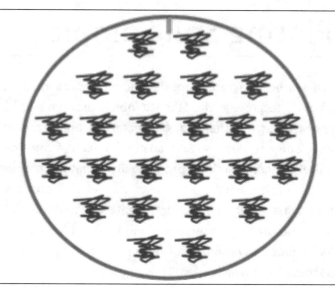

Figure 5. Master plate schematic. This example shows how your plate should look after incubating and allowing the isolates to grow. Patches (in red) were oriented on the plate using a 6x6 grid although smaller ones can be used. Grid was aligned with point of orientation drawn on the back plate (orange vertical line at the top). Notice how patches do not touch – this is critical to prevent cross-contamination.

MATERIALS

- 2 media plates of choice
- Square grid (alternatively, draw grid on back of plates)
- Sterile toothpicks

PROTOCOL

1. Obtain 2 plates containing your media of choice. Label with date, media type, and student and soil sample name around the back edge of the plate. Draw a small vertical line at the edge of your plate as point of orientation.
2. Tape the plate face up on a square grid plate. Align grid with the vertical line on the plate.
3. Using a sterile toothpick, pick a unique colony from your dilution plate (10^{-2} or 10^{-3}). Patch (gently zigzag) colony smear on toothpick onto fresh media plate within the boundaries of one square on square grid. Be careful not to puncture the agar as you smear.
4. Continue to pick and patch colonies onto media plate, each time occupying a new square. Make sure patches do not overlap or touch because this will contaminate the patch, assuming that you picked a single colony. Try to find as many morphologically unique colonies (i.e., different textures, colony margins, and pigments) but do not patch more than 24 colonies per plate to avoid overcrowding.
5. This collection of colony patches will be your master plate.

Plating Soil Sample

We will be using a culture-dependent approach to study bacteria, which relies on the ability of some bacteria to grow in the lab. Microbiologists have used this approach for over a century, and while the premise has not changed, our increased understanding of bacterial nutrition and growth has enabled development of media and lab conditions to more closely meet bacterial requirements for survival. This has also increased the reproducibility of natural phenomena from lab to lab, allowing microbiologists to repeat each others' experiments and confirm observations, thereby advancing the field. While we are far from attaining perfection in culturing bacteria and accurately replicating their natural habitats, we have the tools of observation, inquiry, and ingenuity to come a step closer. In addition, the more we learn about environments like the soil, the more we realize that this is truly an inexhaustible source of bacteria from which we still have much to learn.

After you collect a soil sample, the first step is to suspend the bacteria in liquid so that they can be transferred to another medium (e.g., a nutrient plate), leaving behind plant material, soil animals, and minerals from the soil. It is important to take into consideration the kind of vegetation the soil supported and select appropriate media accordingly. The soil contains a wide range of bacteria, so it is likely to yield growth in almost any standard bacteriological medium.

MATERIALS
- 3 LB plates/group
- Conical tube
- Soil sample
- Spread beads
- Sterile water

PROTOCOL

1. Weigh 1 g of soil sample and place into conical tube or test tube.
2. Determine 3 different ways to plate this sample to visualize microbes.
3. Record all three procedures in lab notebook.

Screen for Isolate Antibiotic Production #1 – Patch/Patch

Alexander Fleming is credited with having discovered the first antibiotic introduced into widespread clinical use, penicillin. In 1928, Fleming made an observation that became the basis for the way microbiologists have searched systematically for antibiotic producing microorganisms ever since. He noticed that a mold (*Penicillium notatum*) that had contaminated a *Staphylococcus* culture was inhibiting the growth of the bacterial cells around it, creating a pronounced "zone of inhibition." This mold secretes its powerful chemical weapon into its surroundings where it diffuses into the broth or agar medium. Susceptible microorganisms that come in contact with this chemical are inhibited in their ability to survive or reproduce. Areas on a plate that would normally be lush with colonies or a lawn of bacteria become clear, creating visible zones of inhibition.

Microbiologists apply these basic principles when conducting activity assays – tests that determine the presence of antimicrobial compounds in a culture. Many researchers are concerned with finding compounds that specifically target bacteria, especially for those that pose a great threat to our health. Therefore, human pathogens or related bacteria (utilized to reduce the risk to the researcher of working with the pathogens themselves) are used as test subjects in activity assays to find compounds that are "active" against them.

THEORY

The patch-patch protocol is a test for antibiotics produced by bacteria that are in close proximity to, but not necessarily in physical contact with, a particular tester strain. This approach assumes that bacteria will synthesize and secrete active compounds independently of their neighboring microorganisms. Many prolific antibiotic producers, such as Streptomycetes, rely on other biochemical and physiological cues to turn on their secondary metabolism, which involves the production of accessory compounds, such as pigments and antibiotics. For example, in *Streptomyces coelicolor*, antibiotic production occurs in a growth phase-dependent manner or in response to nutrient limitation (Bibb, 1996). Therefore, even if susceptible microorganisms are separated by a small gap from *S. coelicolor*, if the secreted antibiotic diffuses toward the tester strain, we should expect to observe inhibition.

REFERENCE

Bibb, M. (1996). The regulation of antibiotic production in *Streptomyces coelicolor* A3(2). Microbiology-UK, 142:1335-1344.

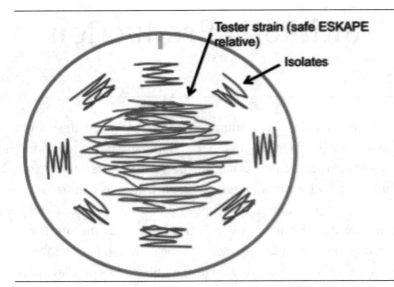

Figure 6. Patch-patch schematic. Isolates that are candidate antibiotic producers are patched around the edge of plate, and a tester strain is patched in the middle, separated by small gap.

MATERIALS

- 2 plates containing media of choice
- Master plates (made in previous experiment) with candidate isolates to be tested
- Plate of safe ESKAPE relative as tester
- Sterile toothpicks

PROTOCOL

1. Obtain your master plate and the culture containing your safe ESKAPE relative of choice.
2. Choose a fresh medium plate to grow safe ESKAPE relative.
3. Pick isolates from your master plate and patch them around the perimeter of the plate (see Figure 6 above).
4. Label each patch with the appropriate name on the back of the plate.
5. Patch your tester strain (safe ESKAPE pathogen) in the center of the plate without touching the patches of soil isolates. Incubate at predetermined temperature and conditions for 1-3 days but no longer to avoid overgrowth. Once patches produce dense growth, make observations or store plates at 4°C until the next lab session.

Screen for Isolate Antibiotic Production #2 – Spread/Patch

THEORY

The spread-patch protocol tests for antibiotic production by candidate isolates that are in close physical contact with the tester strain. In this protocol, the tester strain is spread on a plate, and then, the isolates are patched onto the bacterial spread. If the isolate is active against the tester strain, it should theoretically have no trouble growing on the bacterial spread. Yet, this is not always the case as an antibiotic producer may need time to establish itself on the medium or may not be successful at invading a growing culture of susceptible bacteria. While we can ignore establishment times in this experiment, we cannot ignore that some antibiotic producers may require physical or biochemical contact with other microbes to express genes for antibiotic production. Therefore, this protocol is based on the assumption that microbe-microbe interactions may induce antibiotic production and will increase the chances of identifying a producer.

While this approach is simple, its implications are grand. We know that, in their natural habitats, microbes are part of intricate networks in which they interact with other microbes. Extracellular signals coming from members of the same or different species can unleash a signaling cascade within a cell that ultimately affects its regulation of genes. For many years, researchers have been attempting to find what specific microbe-microbe interactions or other biochemical or environmental cues would trigger the expression of that result in the production of antibiotics and other secondary metabolites.

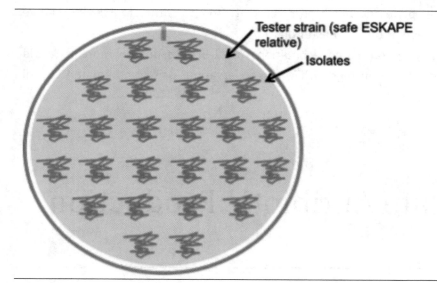

Figure 7. Spread-patch schematic. Isolates are patched (in the same grid arrangement as master plate) onto a spread of safe ESKAPE relative.

MATERIALS

- 2 appropriate media plates (same as master plate)
- Liquid culture of safe ESKAPE relative
- Master plates with isolates
- Spread beads
- Square grid template
- Sterile toothpicks

PROTOCOL

1. Obtain appropriate media plate for your safe ESKAPE relative to grow.
2. Label plate with respective medium, safe ESKAPE relative, and master plate used. Add vertical line as point of orientation aligned with master plate.
3. Obtain a liquid culture of your safe ESKAPE relative.
4. Dispense 150 µL of the safe ESKAPE relative liquid culture onto the medium plate. This is the inoculation step.
5. Spread liquid with L-shaped spreader or add 5-10 spread beads to the plate, being careful not to splash the inoculum. If you are using beads, cover plate with lid and shake side by side to spread the inoculum. Carefully shake the beads off into appropriate container. The liquid should be absorbed into medium within minutes.
6. Place the new plate face up on top of the grid and align line of orientation with grid.
7. Pick isolates from the master plate and patch onto the plate spread with safe ESKAPE relative arranged in the same orientation as on the master plate.
8. Incubate at predetermined temperature and conditions for 1-3 days but no more to avoid overgrowth. Once patches produce dense growth, make observations or store them at 4°C until the next lab session.

Screen for Isolate Antibiotic Production #3 – Top Agar

THEORY

Another method of screening for antibiotic production that we will be using is called top agar. In this technique, liquefied agar is mixed with the tester strain and poured over patches of the soil isolates.

Since the tester strain is uniformly distributed on the overlying agar, which solidifies quickly, it almost allows for the three-dimensional visualization of zones of inhibition.

MATERIALS

- 2 of each appropriate media plates
- Sterile glass bottle
- Liquid culture of safe ESKAPE relative
- Master plates with isolates
- Molten top agar (medium with 50% the amount of agar used in the typical recipe, 0.75%)*
- Square grid
- Sterile toothpicks

*Recommendation: Prepare top agar up to 1 day and at least 2 hours prior to lab session. Ensure medium contains a homogenous mixture of ingredients. Dispense into separate bottles (50 mL) (one per group of students working together; each student will need ~7 mL per plate) and autoclave. The agar will come out fully melted and with minimal water loss. Allow to cool (between 45°C and 55°C) until the time they will be used by the students or place in a 50-55°C water bath for use. Alternatively, microwave bottle of top agar (if made days prior or allowed to solidify) until agar melts but avoid boiling. This alternative runs the risk of water loss, resulting in higher concentrations of agar.

PROTOCOL

1. Patch isolates of interest onto appropriate solid medium for safe ESKAPE relative to grow. Do not use excessive inoculum and patch lightly.
2. Obtain bottle with molten top agar (50%) cooled down to 45-55°C or comfortably warm to the touch. If too hot, top agar may kill cells in the next step. If too cold, top agar may solidify in the bottle.
3. In a sterile glass bottle, mix 100 µL of overnight liquid culture of your safe ESKAPE relative with 7 mL of top agar. Cap bottle and mix contents by swirling.
4. Gently pour top agar with safe ESKAPE relative over the patched plate. Pour onto one side of the plate and tip over to flood entire plate.
5. Cover the entire surface of the plate and let sit until top agar solidifies, at least 10-15 minutes. Incubate upside down (but be sure not to turn the plate over until top agar is completely solid and rigid). Incubate under predetermined temperature and conditions. Incubate for 1-3 days but no more to avoid overgrowth. Once isolates and tester strains produce dense growth, make observations or store them at 4°C until the next lab session.

Safe ESKAPE Relatives Information Sheet

ESKAPE Pathogen	Safe Relative	Culture media	Conditions*	ATCC #
Enterococcus faecium	Enterococcus raffinosus	BHI/ Sheep blood agar	37°C	49464
	Bacillus subtilis	LB	37°C aerobic	
Staphylococcus aureus	Staphylococcus epidermidis	BHI, TSA	37°C aerobic	14990
Klebsiella species	Escherichia coli	NB	37°C aerobic	11775
Acinetobacter baumannii	Acinetobacter baylyi	BHI	37°C aerobic	33305
Pseudomonas aeruginosa	Pseudomonas putida	LB	37°C aerobic	
Enterobacter species	Enterobacter aerogenes	TSA	37°C aerobic	51697
	Erwinia carotovora	LB	30°C	
A positive control for antibiotic producers	Lysobacter antibioticus (10TSA2)	NB/TSA	30°C aerobic or room temp	

*For liquid culture, aerobic means incubate with shaking. *E. carotovora* and *E. raffinosus* should not be shaken.

Notes:
- Ensure non-pathogenic *E. coli* strains are chosen for these experiments.
- For solid culture, all strains should be grown in regular aerobic conditions.
- Gray boxes indicate Handelsman Lab Yale University strains.
- *E. carotovora* grows fairly slowly in liquid culture. Inoculate liquid culture 2 days in advance.
- *L. antibioticus* grows slowly on a plate. Streak out culture 2-3 days in advance.
- *S. epidermidis* grows very slowly in the antibiotic assays. Some dislike using it for that reason.
- All other strains will grow overnight without any problems. For best results, use liquid cultures within 16-24 hours after inoculation.
- *A. baylyi* produces two colony morphologies – opaque and white-colored. Both colony types have been sequenced, and BLAST results indicate that both types are most closely related to *A. baylyi*. Sequence and chromatogram data are available upon request.

Review of Isolates and Activities

What media did you use?

How many colonies were picked for your master plate?

How many of those grew?

What tester strain did you use the first time?

How many active isolates did you have with this tester strain?

What two tester strains did you use the second time?

How many active isolates did you have with this tester strain?

How many active isolates did you streak out?

Table of Isolate Activity Spectrum

Overall spectrum of activity. Fill in isolate name on the top row. You can fill in up to eight isolates in this table, but you may reproduce the table or expand it if you have more isolates. Tester strains (safe ESKAPE relatives) appear listed in the first column. For isolates showing activity (zone of inhibition) against a tester strain, write in a plus sign (+); for no activity (no zone of inhibition), write in a minus sign (−). Include your data in the Small World Initiative Soil Sample Database: www.smallworldinitiative.org/data.

Isolate name								
E. carotovora								
E. coli								
E. raffinosus								
E. aerogenes								
B. subtilis								
P. putida								
A. baylyi								
S. epidermidis								

Serial Dilutions

Adapted from: Jackie Reynolds – Microbe Library

<http://www.asmscience.org/content/education/protocol/protocol.2884>

Determining microbial counts for liquid and solid samples is a common practice in the lab to quantify the biomass of a soil sample, calculate an antibiotic's minimal inhibitory concentration (MIC), or determine the population density in a liquid culture. In most environmental samples, bacteria are numerous, ranging from the tens of thousands to the millions in as little as 1 mL of seawater or 1 g of soil. Given the size of these populations and rate of cell turnover, it would be nearly impossible to get an exact count by counting all the cells directly. Instead of counting cells one by one, microbiologists calculate cell density through colony forming units (CFUs), which give us an approximation of the number of viable cells per milliliter or gram of a sample.

To calculate CFUs, a sample must be diluted in water or a saline solution that keeps the cells in suspension alive. Diluting 1 g of soil with saline solution to a final volume of 10 mL would create a 10-fold or 1:10 dilution of our soil sample; therefore, if the cells are properly suspended in the solution, all the cells contained in 1 g of sample will be evenly distributed in 10 mL of solution. Making serial dilutions of a sample in 10-fold increments allows us to reduce the number of cells per volume to a cell density that is easier to count. Once we have reached a desired dilution of our sample, we can add the dilution to a solid medium that will support the growth of the bacteria. Once the bacteria grow to colonies (1 bacterium giving rise to 1 colony of clones), we can determine how many bacteria were plated and calculate the cell density in the original sample measured in CFUs. For example, if we serially dilute 1 g of soil sample by a factor of 10^3, spread and incubate the dilution on a solid medium, and then observe 130 colonies, we would calculate that there were 130×10^3 or 1.3×10^5 CFUs/g of soil. This number represents the number of viable cells, i.e., cells in an environmental sample that can survive lab conditions and grow in culture. While the proportion of all soil bacteria we can successfully grow in the lab remains low, plating various dilutions on different types of media and under different conditions (e.g., lighting and temperature) can increase our recovery of diverse bacteria.

How to calculate CFU/g soil:

colonies ÷ volume plated (μL) × dilution factor x 1000 μL/mL × volume of suspended soil

For example:

220 colonies on 10^{-3} plate (dilution factor = 1000)

220 colonies counted ÷ 100 μL plated × 1000 × 1000 μL/mL × 10 mL/g

= 22,000,000 = 2.2×10^7 CFU/g

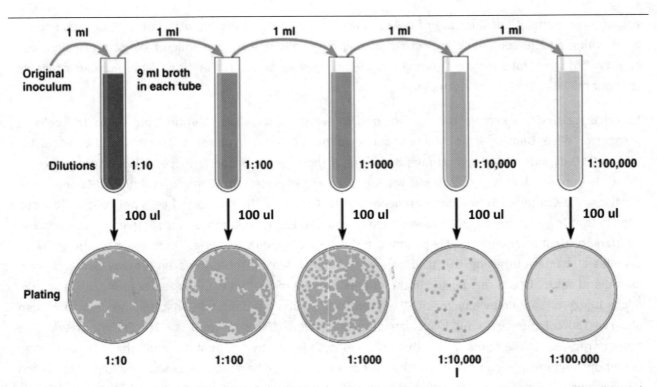

Figure 8. Serial dilution and plating schematic. A series of 10-fold dilution is made from the original inoculum, which contains cells in suspension from the environmental sample. Each subsequent dilution and plate will have 10-fold fewer bacteria than the previous one, making it easier for us to count colonies and calculate CFUs. Photo from Theresa Fischer, Indian River State College.

MATERIALS

- Choice of media plates*
- Conical tube
- Environmental [soil] sample
- Sterile water
- Sonicator or vortexer

*Refer to Media Menu at the end of this protocol.

PROTOCOL

1. Obtain and label appropriate number of plates and 1.5 mL microcentrifuge tubes (one for each subsequent dilution). Dilutions should be made in increments of 10 (10^{-1}, 10^{-2}, 10^{-3}, etc.).
2. Weigh 1 g of soil sample.
3. Transfer to 15-mL conical tube or glass test tube.
4. Add 9 mL of water or isotonic solution, such as 1X PBS, to 1 g of soil.
5. Place tube in sonicator bath and sonicate for 30-60 sec, or vortex.
6. Determine the dilution series and calculate appropriate volumes for each. Again, dilutions should be made in increments of 10, thus add 900 µL of diluent (i.e., water or 1X PBS) into each dilution tube.
7. Remove 100 µL of soil+diluent with micropipette from 15-mL conical tube and add to 900 µL of water/1X PBS in Eppendorf tube. This is 10^{-1} dilution.
8. Mix with vortexer.
9. Remove 100 µL of 10^{-1} dilution and add to 900 µL of water/1X PBS in another microcentrifuge tube. Mix by vortexing.
10. Continue to transfer 100 µL of previous dilution to 900 µL of diluent until reach desired dilution.
11. When finished with dilution series, plate 100 µL of each dilution to appropriate plates.*
12. Note volume and dilutions plated.

*Check with your instructor about spread plating technique.

COMMENTS AND TIPS

Typically plates containing between 30 and 300 colonies are ideal for counting and reduce errors in count estimates. Too high a density of colonies can lead to errors due to colonies overlapping. Too few colonies on a plate can lead to overestimation of counts. Remember to use sterile pipette tips to prepare the dilutions and be sure to change tips between each dilution, which will reduce carryover of cells between samples.

Adapted from:

Reynolds, J. (2005). "Serial Dilution Protocols." Laboratory Protocols. **Microbe Library**. *American Society for Microbiology*. Accessed 17 Oct 2013.

<http://www.asmscience.org/content/education/protocol/protocol.2884>

Serial Dilution Observations and Results Sheet

Pick 1-2 dilution plates from your initial serial dilution on LB and 1-2 dilution plates of your media of choice. Specify the medium in the plate and period of incubation when colonies were counted, e.g., LB at 24 hours. Express your dilution factor (usually a factor of 10) and CFU/g of soil in scientific notation (e.g., 9.7×10^7). Fill and expand the table below as necessary.

Medium / Incubation period	Dilution factor	Volume of dilution plated	Final dilution on plate	Number of colonies	Cells per g of soil (CFU/g)

CFU Practice Exercises

1. You are given a test tube containing 10 mL of a solution with 8.4×10^7 cells/mL. You are to produce a solution that contains less than 100 cells/mL. What dilutions must you perform in order to arrive at the desired result?

2. You have a microtube containing 1 mL of a solution with 4.3×10^4 cells/mL, and you are to produce a solution that contains 43 cells/mL. What dilutions must you perform?

3. You are given a container with 5 mL of a solution containing 5.1×10^3 cells/mL. You are to produce a solution that contains approximately 100 cells/mL.

1) ANSWER: You should perform a series of three 1:100 dilutions to yield 84 cells/mL.

1 mL of original solution to 99 mL of water = 8.4×10^5 cells/mL

1 mL of second solution to 99 mL of water = 8.4×10^3 cells/mL

1 mL of third solution to 99 mL of water = 8.4×10^1 or 84 cells/mL

2) ANSWER: You should perform the following dilutions:

10 μL of original solution to 990 μL of water = 4.3×10^2 cells/mL

100 μL of second solution to 900 μL of water = 4.3×10^1 or 43 cells/mL

3) ANSWER: You should perform the following dilutions:

0.5 mL of original solution to 4.5 mL of water = 5.1×10^2 cells/mL

1 mL of second solution to 4 mL of water = 1.02×10^2 cells/mL or 10^2 cells/mL

Serial Dilution Questions

1. You are given the task to quantify the bacteria in your soil sample. You do a 10-fold serial dilution of your soil sample in sterile water and plate 1/10 of each subsequent (serial) dilution in LB agar plates with cycloheximide – an antifungal and eukaryotic cell inhibitor. If your 10^{-6} (ten to the minus sixth) dilution plate contains 97 bacterial colonies after two days of incubation, how many bacteria do you estimate were present in your initial soil sample (1 g of soil)? Show your calculation and briefly describe each step.

2. Notice this is a three-part question. For each answer, specify the number in the answer box. No need to restate the scenario.

Scenario: If you are determining the CFU of a sample of ocean water, how would the following scenarios (1-3) affect your CFU/mL estimate and the diversity of bacteria you observe:

a) The cells in the sample stick together in clumps.

b) Most bacteria require high salt and minimal nutrients, but you plate them on LB.

c) You make your calculations entirely on 10-fold dilutions, but in your first dilution, you put 10 µL of seawater in 1 mL of water. (Pay close attention to the units.)

3. Is CFU/g of soil a diversity count or an abundance count? How is a diversity count different from an abundance count?

Serial Dilution Answers:

1) ANSWER:

colonies / dilution factor = CFU/g of soil

97 colonies / 10^{-6} = 9.7×10^7 CFU/g of soil

2) ANSWER:

a) You will likely underestimate CFU/mL count. Colonies may contain various genetically distinct cell types. Colonies will merge. Cells may compete for resources and grow disproportionately. You would not get a reliable determination of diversity.

b) You will get a low CFU/mL count (assuming that these cells prefer to grow on high salt, minimal media versus rich media like LB). In addition, fast-growing cells may obscure growth or visualization of those cells preferring minimal nutrients (which are likely to grow more slowly).

c) You have been consistent with the 1:10 ratio. You will underestimate your CFU count by a factor of 10. You may not get a good determination of diversity in your sample.

3) ANSWER:

Diversity – phylogenetically/genetically distinct bacteria, which may exhibit different morphologies, growth rates, metabolites, activity; different species/genera/other classifications; for our purposes – a more qualitative way to look at a sample.

Abundance – [sheer] number of bacteria – more quantitative.

CFU/g of soil is an "abundance" count – entirely quantitative.

Silica Column Chromatography Protocol

In the Thin Layer Chromatography (TLC) section, you used a diagnostic tool that provides information about the polarity of an extract's active components. In this section, you will use the information gathered from the TLC process to guide silica column chromatography, a technique that separates organic compounds into various fractions based on polarity.

Like TLC, silica column chromatography requires a solvent system. However, the choice of solvents for the column is somewhat more complicated; rather than using just a single mixture of solvents as in the TLC protocol, you will now use a progression of increasingly polar solvent gradients. Luckily, the optimal solvent found for TLC can be used to determine the starting point of this progression. In general, it is best to begin the process with a mixture of solvents that is slightly less polar that the optimal TLC mixture. For instance, if a 4:1 hexane:ethyl acetate system proved effective in separating compounds on a TLC plate, you might begin silica column chromatography with a 6:1 hexane:ethyl acetate mixture. From this starting point, you will progress to more polar gradients. For example, a progression of gradients might begin with 6:1 hexane:ethyl acetate and continue with 4:1, 2:1, 1:1, 1:2, 1:4, 1:6, and finally 100% ethyl acetate.

MATERIALS

- 1 glass Pasteur pipette (5 ¾")
- Three-arm stand
- Wooden stick
- Cotton
- Small filter paper
- Silica gel (230-400 mesh)
- Sand
- Pipette bulb
- Solvents making up the optimal solvent system found using the "Thin Layer Chromatography (TLC)" protocol
- Organic extract suspended in the less polar of the chosen solvents
- 8-12 small glass test tubes (numbered)

PROTOCOL

1. Determine the progression of solvent gradients that will be used. This process is discussed above. Your system should have 5-10 different gradients.
2. Secure the Pasteur pipette on the three-arm stand with the tip pointing down.
3. Break off a small piece of cotton and insert it into the top of the pipette. Use the wooden stick to push the cotton down into the top of the narrow tip of the pipette and tamp it down gently. The cotton should be secure enough to stop the escape of silica from the column, but it should not be large enough or tight enough to prevent the flow of solvents through the pipette.
4. Fold the filter paper into a small funnel. Use the funnel to pour silica gel into the top of the pipette. The level of the silica should be halfway in between the cotton plug and the indent near the top of the pipette. Tap the pipette gently until the surface of the silica settles flat.
5. Use the paper filter to add sand. The sand layer should be about 1 cm in height.
6. Put the bulb on the top of the pipette and squeeze slowly and gently. This will help push pockets of air from the column. (**Caution:** Do not release pressure on the bulb while it is still attached to the column. This sudden decrease in pressure will cause the silica and sand to be sucked up the pipette. Always remove the bulb from the pipette before releasing pressure.)
7. Wash the column with the more polar of the two solvents. For instance, if you plan to start with a 6:1 hexane:ethyl acetate gradient, wash with pure ethyl acetate. To do this, use another glass pipette to add this solvent to the top of the column. Add until the solvent reaches the indent near the top of the pipette. Push this solvent through with the bulb so that the solvent level is just above the sand. (Note: Never let the level of liquid in the column fall below the sand. Whenever pushing through solvent or extract, stop just before the liquid reaches the top of the sand.) Repeat once more for a total of two washes.
8. Wash the column with the less polar of the two solvents. For instance, if you plan to start with a 6:1 hexane:ethyl acetate gradient, wash with pure hexane. Repeat once more for a total of two washes.
9. Add the extract suspended in the less polar of your two solvents. Add enough so that the level of the extract is halfway in between the top of the sand and the indent near the top of the pipette. Place your first test tube (#1) under the bottom of the pipette and use the bulb to push the extract down to just above the top of the sand.
10. Remove test tube #1 and replace with test tube #2. Add the first solvent gradient, filling up to the indent near the top of the pipette. Use the bulb to push the solvent down to just above the top of the sand.

11. Switch test tubes and add the next solvent gradient. Repeat this process until all gradients have been added and all fractions have been collected.

Analyzing fractions:
1. Perform a TLC of each fraction and of the raw extract (see "Thin Layer Chromatography" protocol). The stain patterns of the various fractions should "add up" to the stain pattern of the raw extract. That is, each of the components stained in the raw extract should also be visible in the same location on one or more of the fraction plates. (Note: It may not be possible to visualize some of the raw extract's components on the fraction plates due to a low concentration of the compound, for example, if the compound were spread across a large number of the fractions.)
2. Perform an overlay bioassay of all fractions using the procedure described in the "Analyze Extraction for Antibiotic Activity" section of the "Analyzing Organic Extracts for Antibiotic Production" protocol.

Spread Plate

Modified from: Kathryn Wise – Microbe Library (used with permission)

<http://www.asmscience.org/content/education/protocol/protocol.3085>

PURPOSE
One method of distributing bacteria evenly over the surface of an agar plate medium is commonly referred to as the spread plate method. Classically, a small volume of a bacterial suspension is spread evenly over the agar surface by using a sterile bent glass rod, glass beads, or a disposable L-shaped spreader as the spreading device. The goal in evenly distributing the bacterial suspension is typically to permit the growth of colonies that can be enumerated subsequently (see Serial Dilution Protocols) or sampled following incubation. Each plate is spread with a single inoculum of the bacterial suspension. An alternative approach to spreading a single-inoculum volume with a smooth device is to apply a smaller volume and tip the plate, allowing gravity to distribute the inoculum in a band or track (track method) or to allow the inoculum to dry in place (drop method). With this alternative approach, several sample dilutions can be distributed on a single-agar plate.

HISTORY
Since the development of the agar plate in Robert Koch's laboratory, several methods have been used to achieve an even distribution of bacterial growth on or in the agar. The most common methods used to achieve this type of distribution are: spread, pour, thin layer, layered, and membrane filter (Koch, 1994).

PRINCIPLES

Using the spread method, a small volume of a bacterial suspension is distributed evenly over the surface of an agar plate with a smooth sterilized spreader (Koch, 1994). In the case of track plates, gravity is used to spread the inoculum down the agar in a column forming a track (Jett et al., 1997).

PROTOCOL

Agar plates:

Select and prepare an agar medium based upon the type of bacteria to be enumerated or selected. Freshly prepared plates do not work as well as dry plates as it takes longer for the inoculum to absorb into the agar. Plates may be dried by keeping them at room temperature for roughly 24 hours. Plates will dry faster in lower humidity, so placing them in a laminar flow hood will speed the drying process. Once dried, plates may be used or refrigerated in closed bags or containers until required. Refrigerated plates should be warmed to room temperature prior to use.

Inoculations:

When enumerating colony-forming units (CFUs), plates with 20-200 CFUs can be used to calculate the number of CFUs/mL of the original sample. Typically, a dilution series is prepared, often a ten-fold dilution series, using a suitable diluent, such as phosphate-buffered saline.

Serial Dilution Protocols:

A convenient inoculum volume, in terms of spreading, absorption, and calculations, is 0.1 mL (100 µL). Since some bacteria rapidly attach to the agar surface, the inoculum should be spread soon after it is applied. Working from the most dilute suspension to the most concentrated is advised as it is then unnecessary to change pipette tips between the dilutions.

Spreading:

Reusable glass or metal spreaders and beads should be autoclaved prior to use and not reused on different samples. Disposable plastic L-shaped spreaders may be used and disposed of (one for each sample). A reusable glass or metal spreader should be flame sterilized by dipping in alcohol (e.g., 70% isopropyl or ethanol), shaking off the excess alcohol, and igniting the residue. The spreader is then allowed to cool. The spreader is placed in contact with the inoculum on the surface of the plate and positioned to allow the inoculum to run evenly along the length of the spreader. Apply even, gentle pressure as the plate or spreader is spun or rotated. If glass beads are used, ensure they have been properly autoclaved and stored under sterile conditions. Pour 5-10 beads onto a plate either prior to or after the addition of inoculum and shake to evenly distribute until the liquid is absorbed into the plate. Used beads can be washed with soap and water or just rinsed with water prior to autoclaving.

The goal is to evenly distribute the inoculum and allow it to be absorbed into the agar. The plate, or spreader, should be rotated long enough to avoid pooling along the spreader once the rotation is stopped.

Incubation:

After the spread plates have been permitted to absorb the inoculum for 10-20 minutes, they may be inverted and incubated as desired.

Observe the plates before the colonies have had time to fully develop. Closely positioned colonies may be difficult to resolve as separate colonies later, so it may necessary to shorten the incubation period to avoid overgrowth. Incubation in closed humidified containers will help avoid plates drying out when working with slow-growing colonies.

Counting and Selection:

After incubation, inspect the plates. When plating a dilution series, the growth on the plates should reflect the predictable drop in CFUs/plate as illustrated in a 10-fold dilution series prepared from an overnight broth culture of *Escherichia coli*.

COMMENTS AND TIPS

- Make sure plates are sufficiently dry prior to use.
- Plates should be prepared in duplicate or triplicate.
- Do not delay in spreading the inoculum once it has been applied to the plate since some cells will rapidly attach to the agar, especially if the plate agar is dry.
- Avoid spreading the inoculum to the edge of the agar because it is more difficult to inspect and count colonies along the agar's edge.
- Once the dilution series has been made, inoculate plates within 30 minutes to minimize changes in the number of cells in each dilution due to cell division or death.
- Make sure even pressure is applied to the spreader so that fluid is evenly distributed along its length as the plate or spreader is rotated.
- Once the dilutions are made, work backward spreading the most dilute samples first.
- Distributing the organisms by rotating the spreader rather than the plate tends to cause more pooling of the inoculum.

REFERENCES

Jett, B. D., Hatter, K. L., Huycke, M. M., & Gilmore, M. S. (1997). Simplified agar plate method for quantifying viable bacteria. BioTechniques, 23:648-650.

Koch, A. C. (1994). Growth measurement, p. 254-257. In Gerhardt, P., Murray, R. G. E., Wood, W. A., and Krieg, N. R. (ed.), Methods for General and Molecular Bacteriology. Washington, DC: ASM Press.

Streak Plate

HISTORY

The modern streak plate procedure has evolved from attempts by Robert Koch and other early microbiologists to obtain pure bacterial cultures in order to study them as described in an 1881 paper authored by Koch.

The earliest appearance of the three-sector streak pattern (called the T streak) commonly used today may be the 1961 photos published in Finegold and Sweeney (1960). An illustration of how to perform this streak is in the 1968 edition of the Manual of BBL Products and Laboratory Procedures. In addition to the T streak, the BBL Manual illustrates two other streak patterns, neither of which is the simple monodirectional streak pattern used earlier in the century.

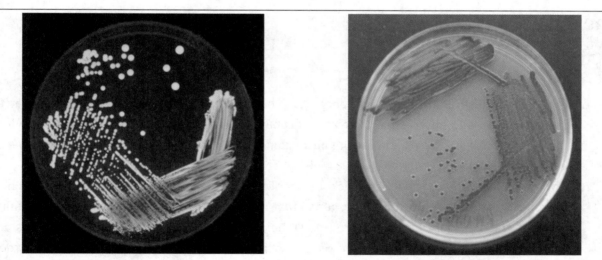

Figure 9. [Left] A four-streak plate, showing the colonies thinning as the streaking moves clockwise. **[Right]** This tri-streak plate shows the single colony isolation of *Serratia marcescens*.

PURPOSE

The purpose of the streak plate is to obtain isolated colonies from an inoculum by creating areas sequentially diluting the inoculum on a single plate. Isolated colonies represent a clone of cells derived from a single precursor cell. When culture media are inoculated using a single isolated colony, the resulting culture grows from that single clone. Historically, most microbiology research and microbial characterization has been done with pure cultures.

THEORY

One bacterial cell will create a colony as it multiplies. The streak process is intended to create a region where the bacteria are so dilute that when each bacterium touches the surface of the agar, it is far enough away from other cells so that an isolated colony can develop. In this manner, spreading an inoculum containing many bacteria will result in the isolation of individual clones.

MATERIALS

- Specimen to be streaked (This protocol is written for a test tube culture.)
- Wooden stick, plastic, disposable transfer loop, or reusable metal transfer loop (usually nichrome, a nickel-chromium alloy, or platinum) (The single-use disposable plastic loop can be discarded between sectors rather than resterilized.)
- Microincinerator
- Sterile Petri dish with appropriate bacterial medium
- Labeling pen
- Sterile cotton swabs (if necessary to remove condensation from the agar surface and from around the inner rim of the Petri dish)

PROTOCOL

1. Label a Petri dish: Petri dishes are labeled on the bottom rather than on the lid. In order to preserve an area to observe the plate after incubation, write close to the edge of the bottom of the plate. Labels usually include the organism name, type of agar, date, and the plater's name or initials.

2. Obtain sterile loop or wooden stick or sterilize a metal transfer loop by flaming in a microincinerator or with a Bunsen burner so that the entire wire is red-hot: When manipulating bacteria, transfer loops and sticks are usually held like a pencil. If plastic disposable loops are being utilized, they are removed from the packaging to avoid contamination and are discarded after a single use into an appropriate container.

3. Open the culture and collect a sample using the sterile loop or the sterile wooden stick: Isolation can be obtained from any of a variety of specimens. This protocol describes the use of a mixed broth culture where the culture contains several different bacterial species or strains. The specimen streaked on a plate could come in a variety of forms, such as solid samples, liquid

samples, and cotton or foam swabs. Material containing possible infectious agents should only be handled by students with the appropriate levels of skill and expertise.

4. Remove the test tube cap: It is recommended that the cap be kept in your right hand (the hand holding the sterile loop). Curl the little finger of your right hand around the cap to hold it or hold it between the little finger and third finger from the back. Modern test tube caps extend over the top of the test tube, keeping the rim of the test tube sterile while the rim of the cap has not been exposed to the bacteria. The cap can also be placed on the disinfected table if the test tube is held at an angle so that settling airborne contaminants do not fall into the tube and the test tube cap is placed with the sterile rim on the table. Insert the loop into the culture tube and remove the loop. Replace the cap of the test tube and put it back into the test tube rack.

5. Streak the plate: Inoculating the agar means that the lid will have to be opened. Minimize the amount of agar and the length of time the agar is exposed to the environment during the streaking process.

   a. Streak the first sector: Remove the Petri dish lid. Touch the loop on the agar in the region of the first sector and spread with bacteria by moving your loop across the dish in a zig-zag manner. Make the loop movements close together and cover the entire first region. The loop should glide over the surface of the agar; take care not to dig into the agar. Discard or flame the loop when this is completed.

   b. Between sectors: Remove the loop from the Petri dish and obtain another sterile loop before continuing to the second sector. Either incinerate the material on the loop or obtain a sterile loop if using plastic disposable loops. The loop must be cool before streaking can continue. Metal loops can be touched to an uninoculated area of agar to test whether they are adequately cooled. If the loop is cool, there will be no sizzling or hissing, and the agar will not be melted to form a brand. If a brand is formed, avoid that area when continuing with the streaking process.

   c. Streak the second sector: Open the Petri dish and insert the loop. Touch the loop to the first sector once, drawing a few of the bacteria (invisible to your eye) from the first sector into the second sector. The second sector is streaked less heavily than the first sector, again using a zig-zag motion.

   d. Obtain a sterile loop for the third sector (see step 2, above).

   e. Streak the third sector: Open the Petri dish and insert the loop again. Touch the loop once into the second sector and draw bacteria from the second sector into the third sector. Streak the third sector with a zig-zag motion. This last sector has the widest gap between the rows of streaking, placing the bacteria a little further apart than in the previous two sectors. Watch closely to avoid touching the first sector as the streak is completed.

   f. Discard or flame the loop to sterilize for proper storage.

COMMENTS AND TIPS

- Alternative streak patterns and different culture media: A variety of alternative streak patterns are possible. Some are used for specific sources of inocula, such as urine specimens. The patterns also differ in the number of sectors as well as in the number of times the loop is sterilized. The four-quadrant streak pattern would be recommended for use when large amounts of bacteria are expected in the inoculum. The extra sector will provide additional dilution and increase the probability of isolated colonies on the plate. The four-quadrant streak plate is described in a variety of references, e.g., in Cappuccino and Sherman's *Microbiology, A Laboratory Manual*, 8th ed. (2008).

- Sometimes, cultures will be streaked on enrichment media or various selective and differential media. For instance, a culture that is expected to have a Gram-negative pathogen will be streaked on a MacConkey agar plate, which inhibits the growth of Gram-positive organisms.

- For reusable loops and needles, an incinerator, such as a Bacti-Cinerator, is used to sterilize the loop. The loop needs to remain inside the incinerator for 5-7 seconds when the temperature inside the incinerator is 815°C. The incinerator will take 5-10 minutes to warm up to working temperature. If not available, a Bunsen burner can be used to flame loops with the appropriate precautions. Avoid contact with the flame and maintain a safe distance from the Bunsen burner at all times. **Do not use Bunsen burners or ignition sources near flammable chemicals.** To sterilize the loop, it should be slowly placed into the flame and kept there until it glows red. Once sterile, the loop should be allowed to cool by holding it still. Do not wave the loop around or blow on it. Flaming loops containing liquids or bacterial colonies can produce aerosols of these materials.

- There are various methods to remove organisms from the loop between sectors. Beginning students are generally taught to sterilize the loop between each sector by incinerating and then cooling the loop. Clinical microbiologists practice a variety of methods. Some flame once after the initial sector and then rotate the loop so that the next sectors can be streaked with an unused side of the loop. Other laboratorians (as clinical microbiologists call themselves) stab the loop several times into the agar to reduce the bacterial load on the loop between sectors.

- Isolated colony appearances: Isolated colonies can be described using the traditional colony descriptions. The Colony Morphology Atlas-Protocol project provides information about bacterial colony appearance and characteristic photographs. The appearance of an organism can vary. For instance, a colony of an organism growing in a crowded sector of the plate will not grow as large as the same organism growing in isolation. The media composition, pH, and moisture, as well as the incubation time and temperature, can all affect the organism's appearance. Colonies selected for subculturing should be colonies that are isolated, i.e., there is no other colony visibly touching the colony.

- Agar with a surface layer of water is not suitable for obtaining isolated colonies. Obvious water drops should be removed from the surface of the plate and from the rim of the plate by using sterile cotton swabs. Plates should be incubated agar side up to avoid condensation that would drop onto the growing colonies on the agar surface.

- Flaming tube mouths: Many protocols suggest flaming the tube mouth before and after removing organisms from a tube. Flaming is often thought to sterilize the mouth of the tube, and this was important when test tubes were capped with cotton plugs. A more important reason to flame the opening of the tube is to warm the air in it, causing it to expand, thereby creating a flow of air out of the tube. This reduces the chance that air, possibly carrying contaminants, will flow into the tube. Only flame glass tubes and use extreme caution.
- Rehearsing the streak procedure: Some instructors have students practice the streaking procedure on a piece of paper. The process helps the student visualize the completed product and practice the fine muscle movements that are required in successful streaking for isolation.
- Students may also find that they can visualize the pattern better if they mark the back of the Petri dish (for instance, a T streak divides the plate into three sectors).
- Before learning to streak, students should have had the opportunity to work with 1.5% agar media. Ideally, they will have had the opportunity to practice using a loop on a plate to determine the best angle of approach and the amount of force required to glide the loop over the surface of the agar without gouging the surface.
- Holding the plate while streaking: If possible, adequate lighting should be available to help the microbiologist follow the tracings of the loop on the agar. For most labs, this means that the Petri dish should be held in one's hand while being streaked in order to reflect the light properly. Additionally, the length of time the Petri dish lid is removed should be minimized in order to limit contamination. There are several ways to hold the Petri dish. Beginning students may find that they obtain the best results leaving the plate on the lab bench and lifting the lid to work. Other students may find that they can place the plate upside down on the workbench and lift the agar-containing bottom, hold it to streak, and then quickly replace it into the lid. Yet other students may have the manual dexterity to manipulate the entire dish in their hand, raising the lid with a thumb and two fingers while balancing the plate in the rest of their hand.

REFERENCES

BBL. (1973). BBL manual of products and laboratory procedures. Cockeysville, MD: Becton Dickson Microbiology Systems.

Buchanan, E. D., & Buchanan, R. E. (1938). Bacteriology for Students in General and Household Science (4th ed.). New York, NY: Macmillan Company.

Cappuccino, J. G., & Sherman, N. (2008). Microbiology: A Laboratory Manual (8th ed.). San Francisco, CA: Pearson/Benjamin Cummings.

Finegold, S. M., & Sweeney, E. E. (1960). New selective and differential medium for coagulase-positive staphylococci allowing rapid growth and strain differentiation. J Bacteriol, 81:636-641.

Lammert, J. M. (2007). Techniques in Microbiology. A Student Handbook. Upper Saddle River, NJ: Pearson/Prentice Hall.

Levine, M. (1939). An Introduction to Laboratory Technique in Bacteriology (revised ed.). New York, NY: The Macmillan Company.

Pelczar, M. J., Jr., & Reid, R. D. (1958). Laboratory Exercises in Microbiology, p. 45-47. New York, NY: McGraw-Hill Book Company, Inc.

Salle, A. J. (1954). Laboratory Manual on Fundamental Principles of Bacteriology (4th ed.), p. 39. New York, NY: McGraw-Hill Book Company, Inc.

Sherwood, N. P., Billings, F. H., & Clawson, B. J. (1992). Laboratory Exercises in Bacteriology and Diagnostic Methods (7th ed.). Lawrence, KS: The World Co.

Williams, C. L., & Letton, H. P. (1916). A note on the preparation of agar agar culture media. J Bacteriol, 1:547-548.
<http://jb.asm.org/cgi/reprint/1/5/547?maxtoshow=&HITS=10&hits=10&RESULTFORMAT=&author1=williams&author2=letton&titleabstract=agar-agar&searchid=1&FIRSTINDEX=0&tdate=3/31/1931&resourcetype=HWCIT>

Williams, H. U. (1908). A Manual of Bacteriology, p. 100. Revised by B. M. Bolton. Philadelphia, PA: P. Blakiston's Son & Co.

Modified from:

Katz, D. S. (2008). "The Streak Plate Protocols." Laboratory Protocols. **Microbe Library**. *American Society for Microbiology*. Accessed 18 October 2013.
<http://www.asmscience.org/content/education/protocol/protocol.3160>

Sulfide and Indole Production and Motility

Adapted from: Clifford Grimsley – Gaston College

SIM medium is a semisolid differential medium, which shows hydrogen sulfide production, indole production, and bacterial motility. Because this medium allows for the movement of bacteria, and not just growth, it will be necessary to use an inoculating needle instead of an inoculating loop to introduce the culture into the tube. Inoculating needles are essentially the same as inoculating loops; however, the wire is straight and is used to stab into the agar medium instead of spreading the bacteria on top of the agar.

Some bacteria produce hydrogen sulfide (H_2S) through the metabolism of certain amino acids containing sulfur or through the reduction of inorganic sulfur compounds in the environment, such as sulfate or sulfide. The hydrogen that is released can be detected by adding a heavy metal salt, such as lead, bismuth, or iron into the medium. Hydrogen sulfide reacts with these compounds to produce black-colored metal sulfides.

Indole is produced when the amino acid tryptophan (yes, the one found in turkey) is metabolized. Indole production can be detected by adding a reagent known as Kovac's Reagent. If indole is produced, the Kovac's reagent will create a cherry red liquid layer on the top of the bacterial culture medium.

Bacteria have evolved several types of motility, but the most common type is driven by a motor that rotates a thick tail, called a flagellum. Motile cells can move throughout SIM medium as it is semisolid, and they will show diffuse growth along the line of inoculation. The production of H_2S is intensified by cultures that are also motile. Therefore, if the culture is both motile and able to produce H_2S, the entire tube may turn black. Motility can also be assessed by creating a hanging drop slide of the culture and observing for motility within.

It is important to test for motility and H_2S production before testing for the presence of indole as the test for indole production may sometimes obscure the observation of the other results.

MATERIALS

- Tubes of SIM media for each isolate and controls per group
- Kovac's reagent
- Cultures of test isolates and positive and negative controls (e.g., *Proteus vulgaris*, *Escherichia coli*, and *Serratia marcescens*)
- Inoculating needle or toothpick

PROTOCOL

Additional Safety Information
Warning: Kovac's reagent contains hydrochloric acid so it should be handled with extra caution.

1. Inoculate each of the cultures, respectively, into separate tubes of SIM media. Stab the wire straight down through the agar to the bottom of the tube and quickly withdraw it along the same path. Do not move the wire around in the agar.
2. Incubate the tubes at the appropriate temperature (25°C for our environmental isolates; some controls may require 37°C) for 24 hours.
3. Examine the tubes for evidence of hydrogen sulfide production (browning or blackening of the media). Record the results.
4. Examine the tubes for evidence of motility of the organism. A motile species grows away from the stab line into the surrounding agar. One can see lines of growth or even a general turbidity

throughout the tube. The growth of a non-motile organism is restricted to the path of the stab. Record your observations.

Semi-solid agar stabbed for motility test.

A. Pattern of growth of a motile organism. Notice the growth lines extending away from the stab line.
B. Pattern of growth of a non-motile organism. Note growth is restricted to the stab line.
C. Perform the Kovac test for the presence of indole as follows:
    a. Pipette 2 mL of Kovac's reagent and add it to the SIM tube being careful not to mix the reagent with the medium.
    b. Observe the color of the Kovac layer and record your results.

Sulfide and Indole Production and Motility Data Sheet

Isolate name	Sulfide	Indole	Motility

End of section adapted from: Clifford Grimsley – Gaston College

Thin Layer Chromatography (TLC)

Using organic solvents, we can extract the active compound from antibiotic-producing isolates (see the "Analyzing Organic Extracts for Antibiotic Production" protocol). However, this extraction process is quite crude, meaning that the result of this process is not a pure active compound, but rather a mixture of many compounds. In order to further isolate the active compound, we can use a series of techniques that separate compounds based on their chemical properties. This process can be guided by the use of Thin Layer Chromatography (TLC) plates.

A TLC plate is a flat glass sheet that is covered on one side with a solid absorbent (often silica). When the bottom of the plate is placed in a mixture of organic solvents, the solvents will flow over the silica and travel up the plate. If extracts are spotted onto a TLC plate, this upward solvent flow will carry with it various components of the extract. However, different compounds will flow at different rates, with nonpolar components generally traveling more quickly and polar components typically traveling more slowly. In this manner, the various compounds that make up the extract can be separated along the length of the plate, with more nonpolar molecules near the top of the plate and more polar molecules near the bottom.

The mixture of organic solvents used in this process (called the "solvent system") can also be varied to achieve different separations of the extract. For instance, the use of a more polar solvent (e.g., methanol) often carries polar compounds further up the plate, meaning that the polar compounds in the extract will be further separated. If a more nonpolar solvent system is used, on the other hand, the result will likely increase separation of nonpolar compounds. In general, a 1:1 mixture of hexane:ethyl acetate is a good starting point for a TLC solvent system. Other common systems include 4:1 chloroform:methanol and 1:1 dichloromethane:ethyl acetate.

Although the compounds contained in organic extracts are often white or colorless, making it difficult to identify the locations of different compounds, there are several techniques that can be used to visualize extract components and to determine which are bioactive. First, various stains can be applied to the TLC plate, resulting in the coloration of particular classes of organic compounds. In the procedure below, we recommend the use of anisaldehyde, a broad-range stain that will result in a wide range of colorations. Other stains, like ninhydrin and potassium permanganate, tend to be more specific. (For instance, ninhydrin stains amino acids and small peptides while potassium permanganate stains oxidizable compounds.) Second, bioassay overlays can be used to determine the movement of active compounds on the plate. In this technique, a thin layer of soft agar inoculated with a bacterial tester strain is laid on top of the TLC plate. After growth under the appropriate conditions, zones of inhibition can be observed, revealing the position of the active compound(s).

MATERIALS
- 2 small silica TLC plates (about 6 cm in height and 2-4 cm in length)
- Organic extract
- 50-mL beaker
- Solvents
- Micropipettes or glass capillary tube
- Black Sharpie marker (as a "control")
- Forceps
- UV lamp
- Anisaldehyde stain (prepared by teaching assistant)
- Heat dryer or hot plate
- LB agar that is half the strength used in normal media (i.e., 75 g/100 mL)
- Liquid culture of tester strain

PROTOCOL

1. Obtain dried organic extract.
2. Resuspend extract in 100 µL of the solvent used in extraction.
3. Draw a thin pencil line on the silica side of each TLC plate about 0.75 cm from the bottom. Be gentle so as not to scratch the silica from the glass surface. In addition, label one plate to indicate which will be used for staining and which will be used for the bioassay.
4. Use micropipette or a thin glass capillary tube to spot 2 µL of extract on a point along the pencil line.
5. Wait for the extract spot to dry nearly completely. Then, once again spot 2 µL of extract at the same point on the pencil line. Continue this process until 10 spots have been placed on the stain plate and 20 spots have been placed on the bioassay plate.
6. Choose another point on the pencil line and gently tap tip of black Sharpie marker on plate until a small black dot is formed. Be sure to get a sufficient amount of ink on the plate but be careful not to pull the silica off the glass surface. The marker ink will act as a control and allow you to visualize movement up the plate with the solvents.
7. Select solvent system and mix solvents in 50-mL glass beaker. The total volume of the system should be 1 mL. For instance, if the 1:1 hexane:ethyl acetate system is chosen, 500 µL of hexane and 500 µL of ethyl acetate should be added to the beaker.
8. Use forceps to gently pick up each plate from the top. Place the plate in the beaker such that the plate sits level (not crooked). The solvent system should cover the bottom of the plate but be well below the pencil line. Cover the beaker with aluminum foil to prevent evaporation of solvents. You should be able to see the solvent line moving upward across the silica.
9. Allow the solvent to run until the solvent front is about 0.5 cm from the top of the plate. At this point, use forceps to remove the plate and gently blot edges with a paper towel. Allow the excess solvent to evaporate completely in the fume hood.
10. Shine UV lamp on the TLC plate prepared for staining and make note of areas of the plate that fluoresce. Try not to shine UV light on plate for more than a few seconds.

For staining of TLC plate:

1. Obtain the anisaldehyde stain prepared by your teaching assistant. **Note:** This stain contains sulfuric acid; handle this stain carefully. Using forceps, pick up the plate prepared for staining by

its top edge. Dip entire plate into anisaldehyde and quickly remove. Plate can be placed on a Petri dish lid or other surface to prevent staining the chemical fume-hood surface.

2. Blot edges of stained plate on paper towel. Dry and heat plate using heat dryer or hot plate until background of plate is light pink and spots of various colors appear. **Note:** Be sure to avoid ignition sources as some of these solvents are flammable. Take pictures shortly after heating as colors may begin to fade.

For the bio-assay plate:

3. Dampen a KimWipe with ethanol and gently wipe the back and edges of the plate prepared for the bioassay. Place this cleaned plate face up in an empty Petri dish.

4. Obtain a liquid culture of a bacterial tester strain of your choice. This strain should be one that was inhibited by your organic extract. Inoculate 12 mL of warm LB agar that is half the strength used in normal media (i.e., 75 g/100 mL) with 240 µL of liquid culture.

5. Pour spiked soft agar into the Petri dish. Swirl gently, ensuring that agar is distributed evenly across Petri dish and that the entirety of the TLC plate is covered.

6. Incubate under appropriate conditions for the tester strain. Keep the Petri dish face up to avoid disturbing the agar.

Further Steps

Observe the results of the anisaldehyde staining and the bioassay overlay to determine how well your chosen solvent system separated the components of your extract. An ideal separation would have compounds spread over the entire length of the TLC plate rather than grouped closely together in one small section of the plate. Adjust the solvent system to try to optimize separation. In general, if the components are closely grouped at the bottom of the plate, make the solvent system more polar. For example, if a 4:1 chloroform:methanol system results in a tight group of compounds at the bottom of the plate, you might make the system more polar by adjusting the ratio to 2:1 chloroform:methanol. If, on the other hand, the components are closely grouped at the top of the plate, make the solvent system more nonpolar. If, for example, a 1:1 hexane:ethyl acetate results in a tight group of compounds near the top of the plate, you might make the system less polar by adjusting the ratio to 3:1 hexane:ethyl acetate. Repeat this process of trials and readjustment until the optimal solvent system is achieved.

Typical Media Menu

This list includes recipes for common microbiological media. Most media come premixed in a dehydrated powder form that is mixed with deionized water. Check which media types are available (ask your instructor) and select a media type to grow your soil sample – you will be using this medium for serial dilutions and to grow your isolate from your dilution plates. Also, pay close attention to their ingredients and how they relate to bacterial nutrition. For more media types and recipes, refer to the Difco "Manual of Microbiological Culture Media" (part of BD Bioscience).

https://www.bd.com/ds/technicalCenter/misc/difcobblmanual_2nded_lowres.pdf

Luria Broth or Lysogeny Broth (LB)
Rich media for propagation and maintenance of *E. coli* used in molecular biology

- Tryptone – 10 g
- Yeast Extract – 5 g
- Sodium Chloride – 10 g
- Agar - 15 g

pH ~7.0

Tryptic Soy Agar (TSA) – in 10% or 50% strength
General medium used for cultivation of a wide variety of microorganisms

- Pancreatic Digest of Casein – 17 g
- Papaic Digest of Soybean – 3 g
- Dextrose (Glucose) – 2.5 g
- Sodium Chloride – 5 g
- Dipotassium Phosphate – 2.5 g
- Agar – 15 g

pH ~7.3

Potato Dextrose Agar (PDA)
Cultivation of yeasts and molds

- Potato Starch – 4 g
- Dextrose (Glucose) – 20 g
- Agar – 15 g

pH ~5.1

All Culture (AC)
For cultivating a wide variety of microorganisms

- Proteose Peptone No. 3 – 20 g
- Beef Extract – 3 g
- Yeast Extract – 3 g
- Malt Extract – 3 g
- Dextrose (Glucose) – 5 g
- Ascorbic Acid – 0.2 g
- Agar - 15 g

pH ~7.2

R2A

Low nutrient (minimal) medium for enumeration and cultivation of bacteria from potable water

- Yeast Extract – 0.5 g
- Acid Digest of Casein – 0.5 g
- Pancreatic Digest of Casein – 0.25 g
- Peptic Digest of Animal Tissue – 0.25 g
- Dextrose (Glucose) – 0.5 g
- Soluble Starch – 0.5 g
- Sodium Pyruvate – 0.5 g
- Potassium Phosphate, Dibasic – 0.3
- Magnesium Sulfate – 0.024 g
- Agar – 15 g

pH ~7.2

Brain Heart Infusion (BHI)

Cultivation of fastidious (fussy) microorganisms, including streptococci, pneumococci, and meningococci

- Brain Heart, Infusion from (Solids) – 6 g
- Peptic Digest of Animal Tissue – 6 g
- Sodium Chloride – 5 g
- Dextrose (Glucose) – 3 6
- Pancreatic Digest of Gelatin – 14.5 g
- Disodium Phosphate – 2.5 g
- Agar - 15 g

pH ~7.4

Todd Hewitt (TH)

Cultivation of group A streptococci or as a blood culture medium

- Heart Infusion from 500 g – 3.1 g
- Neopeptone – 20.0 g
- Dextrose (Glucose) – 2 g
- Sodium Chloride – 2 g
- Disodium phosphate – 0.4 g
- Sodium carbonate – 2.5 g
- Agar – 15 g

pH ~7.8